KU-596-118

VELMA, YOU LEFT OUT THE BIGGEST REASON WILLOWSTOCK IS FAMOUS-- FOR THE BIGGEST ROCK-AND-ROLL GATHERING EVER! THE WILLOWSTOCK FESTIVAL IN 1969!
NOW LEAVING WILLOWSTOCK
'PEACE'
NE COULD ... ORGET THE ... EXCITING ... ENT OF THAT FESTIVAL--

"--When folk rocker ROB NYLON and his band 'His Band' took the stage!"
How many times must we answer the phone before it rings off the stand?
The answer, ol' Bud, is bubblin' in the mud...

RIGHT AFTER THAT, HE RELEASED HIS LEGENDARY ALBUM, "LIVE FROM BIG PUCE"--
UH, FRED, LIKE WHAT'S A "BIG PUCE"?
LIVE from BIG PUCE
Rob Nylon and His Band

IT'S A GHOST!!!

FRED, LOOK OUT!!!
A GHOST!!!
THE MYSTERY MACHINE
SCREEEE

ARE YOU OKAY?!
LIKE, DID HE SAY GHOST?
RHOST?!
SURE, WE'RE ALL RIGHT!

SORRY TO RUN OUT LIKE THAT, BUT WE JUST SAW A GHOST!
YOU'RE ROB NYLON! AND HIS BAND!
YES, AND THIS IS LAVON HOME, HEAD OF HIS B--
HEY, I RECOGNIZE YOU!

YOU'RE THE SCOOBY CREW!
WE ALL HEARD ABOUT HOW YOU SOLVED THE MYSTERY OF THE LITTLE SPRUCE COUPE FOR THE BEACH BUMS!

I'M GLAD YOU'RE HERE! C'MON THIS WAY-- I'M RECORDING MY COME-BACK ALBUM!
WE'RE RECORDING AT BIG PUCE JUST LIKE ON MY FIRST ALBUM.
LIKE, WILL SOMEONE PLEASE TELL ME WHAT A PUCE IS?
REAH!
THE MYSTERY MACHINE

BIG PUCE IS MY HOUSE! WE CALL IT THAT BECAUSE OF THE COLOR!
LIKE, EW.
REAH, REW!

YOU MAY NOT LIKE THE COLOR, BUT YOU'VE GOTTA LOVE THE FULLY EQUIPPED RECORDING STUDIO IN THE BASEMENT.
I'M TRYING TO GET ROB TO RENT IT OUT FOR SESSIONS.
BUT I DON'T WANT TO. I LIKE IT THE WAY IT IS!

SO IS THIS WHERE YOU SAW THE GHOST?
YOU JUST HAD TO SAY THAT WORD, DIDN'T YOU, DAPHNE?
YEP--THE GHOST OF JIMMY HENDRYK-HUDSON, MY GREATEST RIVAL!

WE HAD JUST STARTED TO PLAY WHEN--
Uncool! Uncool! you are too Uncool to make Real Music! Leave Now!!

AT *WILLOWSTOCK*, WHEN JIMMY HENDRYK-HUDSON TRIED TO PLAY GUITAR AFTER YOUR SET-- THE CROWD BOOED HIM OFF THE STAGE!
BRING BACK ROB NYLON AND *HIS* BAND!
BOO!
BOO!

"That's when he said--"
I'LL SEE YOU RUINED IN ROCK AND ROLL, ROB NYLON--
--NO MATTER *HOW* LONG IT TAKES!

YEP, AND THEN HE DISAPPEARED IN THE MIDDLE OF HIS EUROPEAN TOUR!

I JUST KNOW HIS *GHOST* HAS RETURNED TO *SPOIL* MY NEW *ALBUM*!
SO IF YOU PLAYED AGAIN HERE, HE'D REAPPEAR?
I'M *SURE* OF IT!

THEN *I* HAVE A *PLAN* TO UNMASK THIS *"GHOST"*!
FRED, GET THE DISGUISE KIT FROM THE *MYSTERY MACHINE*!
SHAG, SCOOB, YOU FIND THE KITCHEN!
KITCHEN? *THAT* DOESN'T SOUND SO BAD!

OK, HIT IT!

stop!!--

JIMMY!
your music is a DISGRACE!
NOW, DAPHNE!
LEAVE NOW!

LET ME, DAPH! IT'S JUST A GUY IN A MASK--

--R-RIGHT...?
ZOINKS!!!

IF IT'S NOT A GUY IN A MASK--
FLOUR
XXX

"--this FLOUR Shag and Scoob found in the kitchen will show--

--THE BEAMS FROM THE...
...HOLOGRAM...?
RUH ROH!

LIKE, IF IT'S NOT A MASK, AND IT'S NOT A HOLOGRAM, IT MUST BE A--

GHOOOOOST!

GHOOOS--
HUH? SCOOB, WHAT IS IT?
SNIFF SNIFF
RUM RUM! ROOD!

LIKE, NOTHIN' SAYS "LUV" LIKE A VAN FULLA CHOW! LET'S GO, SCOOB!
SNIFF! SNIFF!
LUV
REAH!

I AM THE GHOST OF JIMMY HENDRYK-HUDSON AND I WILL HAVE MY VENGEANCE!
YOU ARE, HUH? WELL, JIMMY WAS THE GREATEST HARD ROCK GUITARIST EVER--

--SO LET'S SEE YOU PLAY AGAINST THE REAL JIMMY HENDRYK-HUDSON!
ROCK ON, DUDE!
WHAT?!

ALL RIGHT! LET'S GROOVE!
STOP IT! STOP!
WOW, FREDDY CAN REALLY PLAY!

I AM THE REAL JIMMY!
NOW HOW D'YOU USE THIS THING AGAIN?

LOOK, JUST SHUT UP FOR A SECOND AND I'LL SHOW Y--

YEEAHHH!!!
NEVER MIND!!! I'M GOING--BUT I'LL BE BACK!
I NEVER KNEW FRED HAD IT IN HIM!
GO FREDDY!

WOOOO!!
EASY, DUDE-- THE GHOST IS GONE!
AND SO ARE SHAG AND SCOOB!
SMASH

SCOOBY-DOO, WHERE ARE YOU?!

RICE? TOFU? LIKE, THIS STUFF CAN'T BE GOOD FOR YOU-- IT TASTES TOO GOOD!
HEY!
JIMMY
RUH-HUH!
BROWN RICE
RICE PUDDING
TOFU
ALFALFA SPROUTS

YOU'RE EATING MY LUNCH!
!
RICE PUDDING

LIKE, SORRY-- WE COULDN'T RESIST--
MUNCH
SLOBBER
SOUNDS LIKE THEY'RE IN THAT OLD VAN!
LUV
STOP! YOU'RE EATING ME OUT OF VAN AND HOME!
NO! MY OAT-BRAN MUFFINS! MY TARRAGON TOFU! MY (SOB) SAFFRON STICKY RICE!
SOUNDS LIKE OUR "GHOST" IS IN THERE, TOO!

IT'S ANY HOLISTIC GURU'S WORST NIGHTMARE! OH, THE HUMANITY!
SLOBBER
GULP
LET ME OUTTA HERE!

THAT'S THE VOICE OF OUR GHOST, ALL RIGHT!
GET HIM!

HE'S GETTING AWAY!

OH, DRAT THESE SANDALS!
TRIP

ALL RIGHT--YOU CAUGHT ME! I GIVE UP!
WHAT ARE YOU--SOME KIND OF FAKE GURU?
FAKE GURU? NO--

--JUST KIND OF A, YOU KNOW, CORRUPT GURU.

I WORK FOR A CORPORATION CALLED KARMACO THAT DEVELOPS NEW-AGE RESORTS ALL OVER THE WORLD. THEY WANTED THEIR NEXT SITE TO BE WILLOWSTOCK--
--WITH THEIR HEADQUARTERS AT BIG PUCE! COSMIC VIBES AND ALL THAT.
SO THEY SENT ME TO SCARE ROB NYLON AWAY FROM THE PLACE!

"I parked near the house when Rob started recording his new album and prepared to project my astral form!"
OHMMM...
LUV

YOU SEE, WE GURUS ALL LEARN HOW TO MAKE GHOST-LIKE IMAGES OUT OF MENTAL ENERGY. SO I DID ONE OF JIMMY HENDRYK-HUDSON--
-- HOPING THAT HIS BIGGEST ENEMY WOULD SCARE ROB NYLON AWAY!
SESAME
VEGGIE BURGERS
Organic Catsup
ALL THAT FOOD IS TO HELP ME CONCENTRATE MY ENERGIES.

UNFORTUNATELY I KNOW NOTHING ABOUT HARD ROCK. I LIKE THE SPICEY GALS. UNTIL GINGERLY LEFT, ANYWAY.
BUT HEY--

-- I'M NOT GOING TO JAIL JUST BECAUSE I LIKE POP MUSIC!
STOP!

CATCH HIM!
DON'T LET HIM GET AWAY!
ALL THAT HEALTH FOOD MUST BE GOOD FOR YOU-- LOOK AT HIM RUN!

KLONG!
OOOF!
BUT HE SHOULD EAT MORE CARROTS. I GUESS HE CAN'T SEE SO GOOD.

HEY, WHAT'S THIS--?

-- IT'S AN OLD LETTER FROM JIMMY!
15¢ POSTAGE?!-- IT MUSTA BEEN IN THIS FORGOTTEN MAILBOX FOR YEARS!

HE SAYS HE WASN'T REALLY HAPPY IN ROCK-- HE STAYED IN EUROPE AND'S BEEN RAISING TULIPS ALL THESE YEARS!
GEE, JIMMY'S NOT A GHOST AFTER ALL!
Dear R
I've le
not

SPEAKING OF GHOSTS--
WHERE'S SHAGGY AND SCOOB?

IT LOOKS LIKE THEY'VE FOUND ENLIGHTEN-MENT!
Z Z
Z Z Z
TOFU

YOU KIDS 'VE BEEN A BIG HELP! NOW THAT YOU'RE AWAKE, YOU WANNA COME WATCH US CUT AN ALBUM HERE AT BIG PUCE?
RIGHT ON!
RIGHT RON!
BUT LIKE, CAN WE HAVE LUNCH FIRST? I'M STARVING!

Howl Scooby Howl At that Big Brass Moon
ROOBY ROOBY ROOOOOOOOO!!!
HAHAHA!
The End

GUEST STARS!

WRITER-CHRIS DUFFY
PENCILLER-MANNY GALAN
INKER-MIKE DeCARLO
LETTERER-JOHN COSTANZA
COLORIST-PAUL BECTIN

VELMA -- THE TOMBOY LOOK IS OLD HAT, BUT IT WORKS.
FRED -- HMPH! I SUPPOSE I CAN WORK AROUND THE BLONDIE THING.
NOW THIS IS MORE LIKE IT, SHAGGY! THE WORD GROOVY SPRINGS TO MIND.
EVEN BETTER! THIS ONE ACTUALLY LOOKS LIKE A DOG!
RANK ROO.

AH, AND YOUR DAUGHTER DORIS IS SIMPLY PERFECT, MR. BLAKE. THESE CLIENTS ARE ACCEPTABLE.
FATHER? "DORIS" WOULD LIKE A WORD WITH YOU.

WHY DO WE NEED A PUBLICIST?!
WE SOLVE MYSTERIES.
DAPHNE, JUST LISTEN. PRESTON CAN PUT MYSTERY INC. ON THE MAP!
BESIDES, HE'S ALREADY CALLED...

"... A PRESS CONFERENCE!"
LADIES AND GENTLEMEN OF THE MEDIA, I HAVE A VERY SPECIAL ANNOUNCEMENT.
FROM THIS DAY FORWARD THE BAND OF HARD-HITTING DETECTIVES KNOWN AS MYSTERY INC...
... WILL HAVE CELEBRITY GUEST STARS! A DIFFERENT ONE EVERY WEEK!
CLAP CLAP
BRAVO CLAP CLAP
WINK
MMPH LIKE, THIS GUY CAN'T BE ALL BAD, MUNCH RIGHT, SCOOB? I MEAN, A CATERED PRESS CONFERENCE! SHLURP HIGH-CLASS!
RIGH-RASS!

The Los Angeles News

RAPPER PUTS CHICKEN MONSTER ON ICE

Doofus' Daring-Do creates new demand for awful albums!

Non-celebrities on-hand to witness

WEEK TWO.
IN THE INCREDIBLE TRADITION OF ITALIAN ICE...
HMM... WHAT'S THIS IN HIS BRIEF-CASE?
HMM...
...THIS WEEK, MYSTERY INC. WILL TEAM WITH VERY SPECIAL GUEST STAR...
ITALIAN ICE
MAMA CAST
HOLLY RINGWORM
MCSMALLY SKULKIN
TONY FLANZA
ROB ROPE
"...SINGER/ SONGWRITER MAMA CAST!"
I HOPE YOU KIDS UNDERSTAND--MY ASTROLOGIST TOLD ME THERE'S NO WAY I CAN FIGHT MONSTERS UNTIL MERCURY IS RETRO-GRADE AGAIN.
OR MY ARMS HEAL. WHICHEVER COMES FIRST.
SO HOW'S IT GOING OUT THERE?
RIKES!
Boston Examiner
MELODIC MAMA TOTALS TECHNO-TERROR!
Adventure Creates Interest in Her Comeback Album
Uninteresting unfamous kids possibly may have helped

WEEK THREE.
WE'RE SO EXCITED ABOUT THIS WEEK'S GUEST!
RIGHT, KIDS?
LIKE, MOST PEOPLE JUST DON'T REALIZE HOW MUCH FOOD FALLS UNDER THE TABLE, SCOOB!
RUH-HUH!
HEY! THIS ISN'T FOOD--IT'S A RECEIPT FOR CATERING "THE KURTIN WEDDING."
THE LUCKY CELEBRITY WHO'LL MASH MONSTERS WITH MYSTERY INC. FOR THE NEXT SEVEN DAYS WILL BE...
"...TEEN-MOVIE ACTRESS HOLLY HEARTWORM!"
UM, HOLLY? YOU'RE SUPPOSED TO THROW THE TRAP BEFORE THE MONSTER GETS THIS CLOSE--
HOLLY?
I CAN'T APPEAR NEXT TO A STRIPED MONSTER IN POLKA DOTS!
I'LL BE RIGHT BACK!
New York Times
ZEBRA ZONKED AT HANDS OF HEARTTHROB HOLLY HEARTWORM!
Offered 3 - Picture Deal in Wake of Heroism
Kids with dog possibly involved, but who cares?

WEEK FOUR.
LADIES AND GENTLEMEN, THIS WEEK WE'VE PULLED OUT ALL THE STOPS--

--NOT ONE, NOT TWO, BUT THREE GUEST STARS--
???
CALL FX GUYS!
ZEBRA TOO FAKE!

--THE DIMINUTIVE McSMALLY SKULKIN--
--THE CHARMING TONY FLANZA--
--AND THE STILL-AMBULATORY ROB ROPE!
THREE OF THEM?!
IT'LL KILL US!
HMM... GATHER 'ROUND, GANG.

I THINK I KNOW HOW WE CAN PUT A STOP TO THIS CELEBRITY INSANITY!
SCOOBY, YOU GRAB THE MICRO-PHONE AND STALL WHILE WE POOL OUR INFORMATION.
gulp RICROPHONE?

THESE THREE BRAVE CELEBRITIES WILL RISK THEIR FAMOUS LIVES BY LEADING INVESTIGATIONS OF PARANORMAL--
EH?
Tap Tap

RICROPHONE, REASE.
HA HA! DOES THE DOG WANT TO SAY SOMETHING?
WHY NOT?

RELLO.
RI'M ROOBY-ROO.
WHAT'D YOU SAY, POOCHIE?

Rooby-Rooby-Roooo!
HA HA HA HA HA HA HA
PRESS

RHAT'S RO RUNNY?
THAT DOG'S A SCREAM! HE ACTUALLY THINKS HE CAN TALK!
HE'S STAR MATERIAL!
"ROOBY-ROO"!
HEY, PRESTON, HOW COME YOU NEVER TOLD US ABOUT THIS GREAT DOG?
HA HA HA HA

YOU DON'T WANT TO HEAR ABOUT THE DOG WHEN THESE THREE GREAT HAS-BEE-- ER, CELEBRITIES ARE HERE! ASK ME ABOUT THEM! ASK ME ANYTHING!
OKAY, PRESTON, I'VE GOT SOME QUES-TIONS!

WHY, IF MY FATHER HIRED YOU TO CREATE PUBLICITY FOR MYSTERY INC. ARE YOU DIRECTING THE PRESS AWAY FROM SCOOBY?
AND WHY, FOR THREE WEEKS, HAVE YOU GOTTEN PUBLICITY ONLY FOR THE LOSER GUEST STARS THAT YOU TEAM US WITH?
I'LL TELL YOU WHY!

YOU'RE BROKE! SHAGGY FOUND THE CATERING RECEIPTS FOR THE FOOD AT THESE PRESS CONFERENCES! YOU'VE BEEN STEALING IT FROM OTHER FUNCTIONS!
OUCH! THE RECEIPTS.

WHY ARE YOU BROKE? YOUR CLIENTS ALL DUMPED YOU--VELMA SAW YOUR FILOFAX! SO WE KNOW THAT THESE "STARS" YOU'VE BEEN TEAMING US WITH ARE YOUR ONLY CLIENTS LEFT!
YOU NEEDED US TO HELP THE CAREERS OF A FEW LAME STARS YOU STILL WORKED FOR.
OOH! THE FILOFAX.

AND FRED SAW YOUR POST-ITS, WHICH PROVE THAT YOU HIRED ALL THOSE SO-CALLED "MONSTERS" WE'VE BEEN FIGHTING THE LAST FEW WEEKS!
AGGH! THE POST-IT.
SAY, YOU KIDS REALLY DO KNOW HOW TO MEDDLE.

PRESTON, YOU WERE ONCE THE TOP OF YOUR FIELD--AND TODAY YOU'VE BEEN BROUGHT LOW BY MYSTERY INC.! BEFORE YOU GO TO JAIL, DO YOU HAVE ANY ADVICE FOR UP-COMING PR PEOPLE OUT THERE?
YES, I DO...

INTERNATIONAL TRIBUNE-HERALD
"NEVER WORK WITH CHILDREN OR ANIMALS" Says Felon!
Preston Pressman skewered by Scooby!
"It almost seems like the dog can talk!" sez Pres!
THE END!

MONSTER MUSEUM

writer: PAUL S. NEWMAN
pencils: JOE STATON
inks: ANDREW PEPOY
letters: JOHN COSTANZA
colors: PAUL BECTON
edits: DANA KURTIN

HEY, SCOOB! COME BACK!
RONE? ROBOY ROBOY ROBOY!

RUMMY!
LIKE, THAT'S NOT LUNCH, SCOOB! THAT'S A MUSEUM EXHIBIT!

RIG RONE! RIG RONE! RUM-MMY!
I HOPE SOME PRO FOOTBALL SCOUT IS WATCHING THIS TACKLE!

ER-- I APOLOGIZE, FOLKS! THE DIPLODOCUS EXHIBIT WILL NOT BE APPEARING TODAY--
GREEEU-UNNNK!!
AAAA! I SPOKE TOO SOON!

THIS CAN'T BE REAL! DINOSAURS ARE *EXTINCT!*
SO ARE *WE*, IF IT *CATCHES* US!
GRUUNK!

FORGET THE *DINOSAUR*, DAPHNE! WATCH OUT FOR THE *AUDIENCE!*
HELP!
RUN!

LIKE, VELMA, YOU'RE RUNNING IN THE WRONG DIRECTION! WHERE ARE YOU GOING?
TO PROVE A SCIENTIFIC THEORY!

GRU--
AS I SUSPECTED --A **HOLOGRAM!**

IT'S *GONE!*
BUT WHO WOULD DO SUCH A THING?
MAYBE WE CAN HELP! OUR *INVESTIGATING TEAM, MYSTERY INC.*, HAS A PHENOMENAL SUCCESS RATE!
ER--UP 'TIL NOW!

SOUNDS GOOD! BUT FIRST--
CALLING ALL SECURITY! THIS IS THE DIRECTOR! SOMEONE HAS STOLEN OUR DIPLODOCUS!
NO ONE LEAVES THE MUSEUM WITHOUT FIRST BEING SEARCHED!

YOU HEARD THE DIRECTOR, COVER ALL EXITS! CHECK EVERY-ONE FOR BONES!
ME? I'M A GUARD, NOT A DOCTOR!

HOLD IT, EVERYONE! YOU NEED TO CLEAR SECURITY!
EXIT
BUT-- THE MONSTER!

WHAT'S THE BIG IDEA?
LET US OUT!
BOY, LOOKS LIKE SECURITY SURE HAS A BONE TO PICK WITH THESE PEOPLE!
EXIT
RUH-HUH!

BUT, MR. DIRECTOR, NO ONE PERSON COULD SNEAK OFF WITH ALL THOSE BONES!
GRUMBLE MUTTER
AH! BUT THERE MIGHT BE A CONSPIRACY WITH LOTS OF PEOPLE TRYING TO WALK OFF WITH A FEW BONES EACH!

ALL RIGHT, YOU'RE CLEARED!
SO FAR, NOT A SINGLE MISSING BONE! IT MAKES NO SENSE!
THAT DINOSAUR HOLOGRAM IS A MAJOR CLUE! VELMA, GET THE OTHERS--
--LET'S INVESTIGATE!
YIKES! YOU ON TO SOMETHING, SCOOB?
REAH!
RIS RUN! RIS RUN!
ZOINKS!
SEARCH HIS DISPATCH CASE!
N-NO! PLEASE!
ALL I HAVE IN HERE IS A HAM SANDWICH!
OH, NO, SCOOB! YOU'RE SUPPOSED TO BE LOOKING FOR BONES, NOT BALONEY!
SAY, DOES THAT COME WITH PICKLES AND ONIONS?
SLURP!

SECURITY IS GETTING NOWHERE. LET'S SPLIT UP!
DAPHNE AND I WILL GO ONE WAY. VELMA, SHAG AND SCOOB, YOU CHECK THE OTHER PART OF THE MUSEUM!

DOESN'T LOOK LIKE ANY BONES ARE HIDDEN HERE!
BUT WHAT A FUN PLACE TO LOOK!
Gem ROOM
Herkimer DIAMOND

FRED, IF ANYONE'S EVER STUCK FOR AN IDEA OF WHAT TO GET ME, THIS'LL DO JUST FINE!
Hopedfore DOUBLE DIAMOND
YEAH, BUT THEN WE'LL BE STUCK FOR THE BILL!

Bird ROOM
NOTHING HIDDEN HERE EITHER!
YEAH, ALL I SEE ARE--

--VAMPIRES?!

DAPHNE, WHERE ARE--
THEY MUST BE HOMING IN ON THE PAPER CUT I GOT FROM THE MUSEUM TICKET! RUN, FRED!

BACK! YOU'RE NOT MAKING DAPHNE ANEMIC, PAPER CUT OR NO PAPER CUT!
CLIK

GONE!
MUST BE ANOTHER HOLOGRAM! BUT WHO IS CREATING THESE HOLOGRAM MONSTERS-- AND WHY?

WELL, WE BOTH LEARNED OUR LESSON! NO SILLY HOLOGRAM VAMPIRE'S GOING TO SCARE ME AGAIN!

EEE!
NOW MUMMIES-- THAT'S A DIFFERENT STORY!
EGYPTIAN
EASY, DAPH! THEY'RE JUST MORE HOLOGRAM MONSTERS, BUT HOW DO WE TURN THEM OFF?
GRARR!

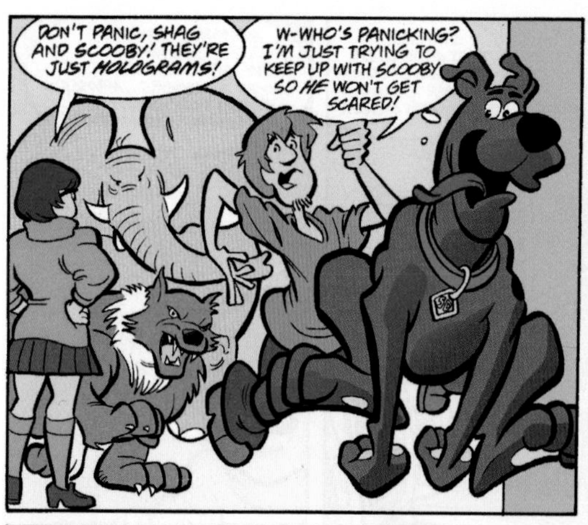
DON'T PANIC, SHAG AND SCOOBY! THEY'RE JUST HOLOGRAMS!
W-WHO'S PANICKING? I'M JUST TRYING TO KEEP UP WITH SCOOBY SO HE WON'T GET SCARED!

WHAM
LIKE, OOOPS!

DID YOU RUN INTO SOME HOLOGRAMS, TOO?
LIKE, BEFORE OR AFTER WE RAN INTO YOU?

ZOINKS! NOW EVEN THAT LAST BONE IS GONE! DID YOU TAKE IT, SCOOB?
RUH-UH! ROT RE!
THE MYSTERY DEEPENS!
WHICH CALLS FOR SOME DEEP THINKING--

VELMA, THAT DOESN'T LOOK VERY DIGNIFIED!
RELAX, DAPHNE! A CLUE-CHASING DETECTIVE HAS TO GET DIRTY ONCE IN A WHILE!
AHAH! JUST AS I SUSPECTED--

A WIRE! NOW TO FIND OUT WHERE IT LEADS TO!
LOOK AROUND FOR MORE CLUES, GUYS --I'M GOING TO FOLLOW THIS CLUE!

THIS WIRE GOES UNDER THAT DOOR! SO WHERE DOES *THAT* LEAD TO?

JINKIES! THAT COMPUTER MUST HAVE ENOUGH POWER TO RUN THE *PENTAGON!*

HMMM... "CONTROL PROJECTION PANELS... MOVEMENT AGITATORS... ROOM NUMBERS...NAMES... DINOSAUR ROOM... MUMMY CHAMBER--"
IT'S *ALL* SET UP TO DISPLAY *HOLOGRAMS!*

CREEEAK
FRED? DAPHNE? IS THAT *YOU?*

HEY! WHO'S THERE?

GONE! BUT I *BET* WHOEVER THAT WAS, WAS COMING IN TO WORK THE *HOLOGRAM COMPUTER!*

I THINK THE BEST PLACE TO FIND MORE CLUES IS THE CAFETERIA, RIGHT, SCOOB?
CAFETE
REAH, REAH!

SCOOB? THE CAFETERIA'S THIS WAY!
RUH-UH! RIS RAY!
CA

WHAT'S SO FASCINATING ABOUT THAT OLD INDIAN WAR CANOE? LIKE, YOU'RE JUST BARKING AT BARK!
DUGOUT CANOE
ROOK! RUMMY!

LIKE, HELLOOO! COMING ABOARD--

BINGO, SCOOB!
YOU FOUND THE BONES!
BUT, LIKE, I STILL DON'T THINK YOU CAN EAT THEM.
RAWWW...!

EXCUSE ME, SIR-- I THINK THE GANG AND I HAVE *SOLVED* YOUR MYSTERY!
SOLVED IT? WONDERFUL! *WHERE* ARE THE MISSING BONES?

AIEEEEEEEE!
MUMMIES! MONSTERS! AND NOW A *BANSHEE*?

AIEEEEEEEE!
IT'S MORE FRIGHTENING THAN THAT! IT'S THE *ALARM* -- SOMEONE HAS STOLEN THE HOPED-FORE *DOUBLE DIAMOND*!
Gem ROOM

GONE! AND IT'S WORTH MILLIONS AND TRILLIONS AND ZILLIONS!
I-IT'S MY FAULT! PROTECTING IT WAS MY RESPONSIBILITY! HERE, SIR, I'M TURNING IN MY BADGE!

YOU CAN'T, CHIEF, NOT WHEN WE NEED YOU MOST!
NO, SIR! IT'S THE RIGHT THING TO DO! TAKE MY BADGE!
PSSST! GUYS!
CHIEF
SECURITY

GUYS, WATCH THE *CHIEF*!
I'M GOING TO DO SOME HOLOGRAM MAGIC OF MY OWN!

I-I FAILED THE MUSEUM! FAILED THE DIRECTOR'S TRUST!
TAKE IT EASY, CHIEF, SUCH A BIG DIAMOND CAN'T JUST VANISH!

SEE? IT'S BACK!
WHAT?!

IT CAN'T BE!--
--BECAUSE IT SHOULD BE IN YOUR POCKET! RIGHT?

YOU'RE NOT TURNING ME IN!
HEY!
OW!
OWW!
LIKE, DOUBLE OWW!

STOP HIM!

HE HAS THE DOUBLE DIAMOND!

HUFF! PUFF!

YOU CAN'T SCARE ME!
I CREATED THESE HOLOGRAM MONSTERS! I'LL RUN RIGHT THROUGH ALL OF YOU!

HUH? TH-THIS ONE'S SOLID?!
YEOOW!

STAY ON TOP OF HIM, SCOOB! JUST DON'T LICK HIM TO DEATH!
REH HEH HEH!
SLURP!
SLURRRP!

ZOINKS! TALK ABOUT LOSING FACE!
HEY! DON'T!

WHY, HE USED THIS MASK TO POSE AS THE CHIEF! BUT WHERE IS THE REAL CHIEF?

I DON'T KNOW ABOUT THE REAL CHIEF, BUT HERE'S THE DOUBLE DIAMOND! IT FELL OUT OF HIS POCKET WHEN HE TRIPPED!
SOMEONE CHECK OUT THAT BROOM CLOSET!
MM! MMPH!
SUPPLIES

CHIEF!

ANOTHER CASE SOLVED! YOUR CUNNING PLOT TO USE MONSTER HOLOGRAMS TO DIVERT ATTENTION FROM THE GEM ROOM FAILED.
I'D HAVE GOTTEN AWAY WITH IT, IF IT WEREN'T FOR THOSE MEDDLING KIDS!
THANKS, GANG! NOW ALL I HAVE TO DO IS FIND A WAY TO REPAIR THE DINOSAUR SKELETON.

THERE'S YOUR MODEL-- THE HOLOGRAM!
CLIK
A FEW DOZEN BONES ARE NO PROBLEM FOR THIS COMPUTER!

MANY RESET BONES LATER...
LIKE NO, SCOOBY! NOT AGAIN! HOW MANY TIMES DO I HAVE TO TELL YOU-- THOSE BONES ARE FOR VIEWING, NOT CHEWING!
HA HA HA HA HA HA HA
ROOBY ROOBY ROOO!
The End

READY FOR HOLIDAY SHOPPING, GANG?
IT'S SO HARD TO SHOP FOR MY FATHER. HOW DO YOU GET SOMETHING FOR THE MAN WHO HAS EVERYTHING?
LIKE, I KNOW, DAPHNE--
Season's Greetings

-- THE NEW "MIGHTY MITE BYTES II" VIDEO GAME!
THAT'S WHAT A REAL FRIEND WOULD GET THEIR PAL -- I MEAN, DAD! RIGHT, SCOOB?
REAH, REAH! RIGHTY RITES!

LIKE, A SWEATER, VELMA? WOULDN'T "THEY" RATHER GET MIGHTY MITE BYTES II?
RUH-HUH!

HEY, "THE WORLD'S GREATEST UNSOLVED MYSTERIES"!
LOOK! "TIPS ON MIGHTY MITE BYTES II"!
GEE, IF ONLY I HAD THAT GAME...

SAY, SCOOB, HAVE YOU HEARD OF THE NEW MIGHTY MITE BYTES GAME? THAT'S SPELLED M-I-G--
SHAGGY, WE KNOW! WE KNOW!

BURGER MAX
LIKE, I'M JUST TRYING TO HELP!
TAKE IT EASY, GUYS! HERE, MAYBE SOME SCOOBY SNACKS WILL LIFT YOUR HOLIDAY SPIRITS!
SCOOBY SNACKS
ROOBY RACKS! ROBOY OBOY OBOY!

I KNOW SHAGGY WANTS IT--
--BUT IT'S IMPOSSIBLE TO FIND THAT GAME!
MUNCH MUNCH
WE'VE LOOKED EVERYWHERE!
I CALLED EVERY STORE, CHECKED THE NET, EVEN LOOKED FOR A BOOTLEG COPY! NO ONE HAS ONE!

IT'S STRANGE, GANG! ALMOST A--
--MYSTERY!
LIKE, LOOK, SCOOB!
RASP!

HUH?!
MIGHTY MITE BYTES II! THE PERFECT GIFT FOR THE SPECIAL SOMEONE!
RIDEO RAMES! RAY!
MIGHTY MITE BYTES II
The Ghost of Christmas Presents
writer: JOHN ROZUM
artist: TIM HARKINS
letters: JOHN COSTANZA
colors: PAUL BECTON
ghosts: DANA KURTIN & CHUCK KIM

LIKE MIGHTY MITE BYTES IS IN AISLE 3 UNDER "M."
I'LL BE IN AISLE 5 SO I WON'T SEE IF ANYONE LIKE, HAPPENS TO BUY ME A PRESENT!
MAYHEM

EXCUSE ME, DO YOU REALLY HAVE MIGHTY MITE BYTES II?
YEP! WE GOT THE ONLY SHIPMENT! THEY WOULDN'T EVEN RELEASE WHAT THE VILLAIN LOOKED LIKE UNTIL NOW.
WE'RE ABOUT TO START OPENING THE BOXES, SO IF YOU WANT ONE...

...YOU'D BETTER GET IN LINE!
LINE STARTS HERE
THE ONLY MYSTERY HERE IS HOW LONG WE'LL HAVE TO WAIT!

LIKE, CHECK THIS OUT, SCOOB.
"BATTLE CRIME WITH THE HEROIC BLUE FALCON AND HIS CYBERNETIC WONDER DOG, DYNOMUTT!"
WHAT'LL THEY THINK OF NEXT?
BYTES
REE-HEE-HEE-HEE!
NEW

HEY, HERE'S ONE WITH A TALKING SHARK!
WILD, HUH, SCOOB?
RUH... RAGGY...?
KREE! KREE!

ZOINKS!!! A MIGHTY MITE!
REEELP!

RUN, SCOOB!
SKID
SKID

BONK
BLUE FALCON

THANKS, BLUE FALCON! I OWE YOU ONE!

YIKES!
SKREE! SKREE!
OH NO-- I KNEW I SHOULDN'T HAVE MENTIONED THE M-WORD!
WELL, AT LEAST THERE'S NO LINE ANY-MORE.
LIKE, I WANTED TO PLAY MIGHTY MITE BYTES II-- BUT NOT AS THE BYTE!
RUN FOR YOUR LIVES!

WAIT, COME BACK! IF YOU DON'T BUY THIS GAME, I'LL GO OUT OF BUSINESS!
WHAT A STRANGE PROMOTIONAL GIMMICK! USUALLY YOU WANT TO ATTRACT CUSTOMERS--
--NOT SCARE THEM AWAY!
MIGHTY MITE BYTES

IT'S NO GIMMICK!
NO ONE IS SELLING THE GAME--BECAUSE OF THAT GHOST!

GHOST?!
RHOST?!

IT WOULDN'T LET THE DRIVERS EVEN LEAVE THE GAME FACTORY!
ONLY ONE TRUCK GOT THROUGH-- TO MY STORE! BUT THE GHOST CAME WITH IT!

LIKE, OH NO! I HADDA WANT A HAUNTED CHRISTMAS PRESENT!
COME ON, SHAGGY!
LET'S SOLVE THIS MYSTERY! WILL YOU DO IT FOR-- A SCOOBY SNACK?
SCOOBY

ALL RIGHT, YOU TALKED ME INTO IT. LET'S GO, SCOOB!
REAH! SLURRRP!

OKAY GANG, LET'S SPLIT UP.
VELMA, SHAGGY, AND SCOOB, CHECK THE AISLES.
DAPHNE AND I WILL LOOK FOR CLUES IN THE STORE-ROOM.

HMM!
LIKE, QUIT PLAYING WITH THAT RED FELT, VELMA! THIS IS SERIOUS!
THERE'S A VIDEO GAME AT STAKE!

SKREEE!
YIKES!

LIKE, I SAID I WANTED TO PLAY THIS GAME--

SKREE!
--NOT LIVE IT!

SHAGGY, HOW DO YOU STOP THIS THING?
WELL, BY SPITTING FIRE OR GROWING PLANTS OR--

--OPENING DOORS.
WHUDD!

MOAN... MY HEAD!
DOES THE GHOST DO THAT IN THE GAME?
NO, BECAUSE THIS ISN'T A GHOST!

RIGHT! IT'S THE MAN WHO CREATED MIGHTY MITE BYTES!

THE RED FELT I FOUND HAD TO COME FROM A COSTUME.
AND ONLY SOMEONE WHO KNEW WHAT THE TOP-SECRET VILLAIN LOOKED LIKE COULD MAKE A COSTUME OF HIM!

PLUS IT HAD TO BE SOMEONE WHO HAD A PERSONAL STAKE IN STOPPING THE GAME FROM SHIPPING--
--AND THIS MAGAZINE IN THE STOREROOM SAID THE PROGRAMMER SPLIT WITH THE COMPANY OVER THE GAME!
BYTES CREATOR BITES DUST

THAT'S RIGHT!
THEY WERE SHIPPING THE GAME FOR CHRISTMAS EVEN THOUGH IT HAD BIG PROBLEMS!

THE GAME'S NO GOOD?
LIKE, OH NO!
I DIDN'T MEAN ANY HARM--I JUST DIDN'T WANT ALL THOSE KIDS TO GET ROTTEN GAMES.
WELL... IT IS THE HOLIDAYS, AND NO ONE GOT HURT. BUT NEXT TIME, WORK OUT YOUR PROBLEMS FACE TO FACE--NOT AS A GHOST!

WELL, WHAT ARE WE GOING TO GIVE SHAGGY FOR CHRISTMAS NOW?
TELL YOU WHAT!
HERE'S THE PROTOTYPE OF MY NEWEST GAME--
--YOU CAN TEST PLAY IT FOR ME.
MIGHTY MITE BYTES II
OH BOY!
THIS IS THE BEST PRESENT EVER!

I'M ALWAYS LOOKING FOR IDEAS FOR NEW GAMES!
FOUR MYSTERY-SOLVING KIDS AND A DOG...
...HMMN! HAS POTENTIAL!
ZOINKS! HIGH SCORE!
ROOBY ROOBY ROO!
HAHAHA!!
THE END

WE'RE NOT GOING TO MAKE IT--!

--WE'RE NOT GOING TO MAKE THE 6AM FERRY TO TERROR ISLAND! WE'LL NEVER MEET DAPHNE AND FRED TOMORROW MORNING NOW!
ANY LUCK WITH THAT MAP, SHAG?
UMMM...

I GUESS SCOOB AND I, LIKE, USED THE OLD MAP AS A NAPKIN A FEW TOO MANY TIMES. SORRY, VELMA.
RORRY.

NEVER MIND! HERE IT IS -- ROUTE 1313!
LIKE, THIS DETOUR IS CREEPY-LOOKING, VELMA.
ROUTE
1313
BEWARE

OH, COME ON, SHAGGY! IT'S JUST AN OLD STATE HIGHWAY!
HERE, YOU DRIVE. I'M POOPED! WAKE ME UP WHEN WE GET TO THE FERRY.
RIGHTY-RIGHT, RELMA.
GULP!

SOON...
WELL, SCOOB, MAYBE I WAS WRONG ABOUT THIS SHORT CUT. IT'S BEEN, LIKE, SMOOTH DRIVING!
LIKE, WE'VE GOT THE NIGHT WIND BLOWING IN OUR HAIR AND FUR, LOTSA SNACKS...
...NO TRAFFIC, LOTSA SNACKS, THE MONSTER HITCHHIKING ON THE SIDE OF THE ROAD, LOTSA SNACKS...
ZZZZ
AAAAAA!
BEWARE
SCOOBY-DOO IN
ARE WE SCARED YET?
Story: CHRIS DUFFY
Pencils: MANNY GALAN
inks: MIKE DeCARLO
lettering: JOHN COSTANZA
coloring: PAUL BECTIN
edits: DANA KURTIN

GOING MY WAY?
RIPES!
S-SORRY, BUT I DON'T THINK SO!!
VROOOM
VELMA, LIKE, WAKE UP!
THIS GROSS GREMLIN HITCHHIKER JUMPED ON THE WINDSHIELD--
REAH! REAH! REMLIN!
TOLL
VERY FUNNY, GUYS. YOU WOKE ME UP FOR THIS?
HEY, LOOK OUT! WE'RE COMING TO A TOLL!

EIGHTY-FIVE CENTS, PLEASE.
GHOST
MURDER
DEATH
DEMON
ZOMBIE
SERIAL KILLER
H-HERE Y'GO, GUY.

FIRST A GREMLIN, NOW A CREEPY CLERK!
LIKE, WHAT IS UP ON THIS ROAD?

OH, SHAGGY, IT'S JUST YOUR IMAGINATION! JUST GET US TO THE FERRY--
AND TRY NOT TO WAKE ME UP AGAIN, OK?
OKAY, OKAY!
SNACKS
SOON
ROO-ROO ROO-ROO!
LIKE, AT LEAST WE STILL GET THE COOL RADIO STATIONS!
I don't wanna wait... for LUNCH to be OVER...
WE INTERRUPT THIS FOOLISH MUSIC FOR THE FOLLOWING ANNOUNCEMENT!
?!
ZZZZ
THE MORTALS TRAVELLING ALONG ROUTE 1313 ARE DOOMED--
--UNLESS THEY GET OFF THE ROAD IMMEDIATELY!

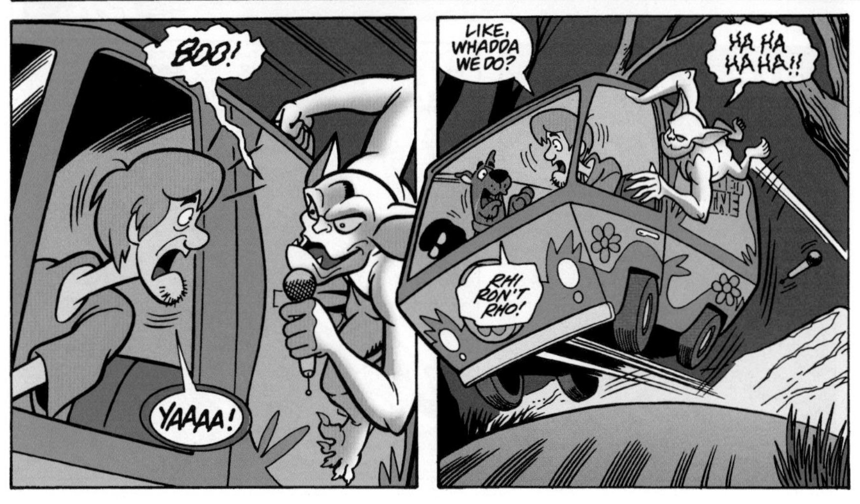
BOO!
YAAAA!
LIKE, WHADDA WE DO?
HA HA HA HA!!
RHI RON'T RHO!

ZOINKS!
YOU WERE WARNED!

SWIPE!
YIPE!
UH... HAVE SOME SNACKS?
?
SNACKS

WHAM
LIKE, LOOK OUT FOR THE--
--CONSTRUCTION SIGN...

YAWN! WHAT'S GOING ON? WHY ARE WE STOPPING?
BECAUSE THAT, LIKE, *IMAGINARY* GREMLIN JUST, LIKE, ALMOST CHOPPED OFF MY *IMAGINARY* *HEAD!*
WORSE, HE SWIPED OUR SNACKS!
RUH RORROR... RUH RORROR!

ZEKE'S Quik Shop
SHAGGY, THIS PLACE IS DESERTED!
WE GOTTA HAVE SNACKS--HAUNTED HIGHWAY OR NO HAUNTED HIGHWAY! WE GOTTA REFUEL!
THE MYSTERY MACHINE

A CUSTOMER! AT LAST!
REFUEL, YOU SAY?
YEAH, BUT NOT THE TANK--US!

OH. MAYBE MARTY CAN HELP YOU. HE'S THE ONLY OTHER BUSINESSMAN LEFT IN THESE PARTS!
HMM?... WHEN DID WE PICK UP THIS MAGNET?
TEXAS
YAWN

I'M MARTY. YOU WANT TO BUY A SOUVENIR?
LIKE, YEAH, IF WE CAN EAT IT! WE NEED SOME SNACKS!
REAH! RACKS! SCOOBY RACKS!
THE MYSTERY MACHINE

SNACKS, HUH? HAVEN'T HAD ANY OF THOSE SINCE THE LAST TANKER DRIVER LEFT HIS TRUCK ON THE ROAD SOMEWHERE AND RAN OFF ON FOOT!
NOBODY GETS THROUGH ROUTE 1313 THESE DAYS--BECAUSE OF THE GREMLIN!
ZOINKS!
AMERICA IN MAGNETS
REMLIN!

'COURSE I DON'T BELIEVE IN THE GREMLIN. THAT'S WHY I'VE KEPT MY BUSINESS GOING.
HMM... NO SNACKS IN HERE.

BUT I DO HAVE SOME SCENTED CANDLES.
LIKE, THAT'S OKAY, MAN.
PHEW!
YAWN

MAN! LIKE, NOW I'M SUPER-HUNGRY AND SUPER-SCARED! WHAT IF THAT GREMLIN COMES AFTER US AGAIN?

YAWN C'MON, GUYS, WE'RE ALMOST THERE! THE GREMLIN'S OBVIOUSLY SOME URBAN LEGEND.
NOTHING'S GOING TO HAPPEN. I'M GOING BACK TO SLEEP.
LIKE, OKAY. IF YOU HEAR A NOISE IT'S PROBABLY JUST MY STOMACH GRUMBLING.
ROR RUH REMLIN!

LIKE, VELMA'S RIGHT, SCOOB. ONLY A FEW MORE MINUTES ON THIS TREACHEROUS TURNPIKE!
RHAT A RELIEF!
WE MAY BE STARVING, BUT WE CAN SAY GOODBYE TO THAT CREEPY--
EXIT TO TERROR ISLAND FERRY 10 MILES

MOO-HOO-HOO-WHA-HA-HA-HA!
--GREMLIN.
THE MYSTERY MACHINE
GRRRMMMM

I CAN'T LOOK!
YOU DRIVE, SCOOB!
???

!!!

ARE WE LOSING HIM?

LIKE, QUICK! WHAT'S HAPPENING?
ROOBY RACKS!
YEAH? COOL!
VROOM!

SUPER SNACKS
YOW! WHO TAUGHT YOU TO DRIVE?!
ROO RID.
OH YEAH.
RRRM!
SCREEEE

LIKE, TOO BAD NOBODY TAUGHT HIM!

ROOBY ROO!
munch munch I'D DO ANYTHING FOR A SCOOBY SNACK!
EVEN gulp! UN-MASK THE GREMLIN AS THAT CREEPY--

--MARTY?!
YES, I'VE BEEN TRYING TO CATCH HIM FOR MONTHS!

HUH?! THE TOLLBOOTH GUY?
NO, OFFICER TOLLIN!
I WAS WORKING UNDERCOVER IN THAT TOLL-BOOTH, TRYING TO CATCH THE GREMLIN!

I WAS SICK OF ALL THE TRAFFIC ON THE ROAD! SO I MADE A COSTUME FROM GIFT SHOP STUFF TO SCARE PEOPLE AWAY FROM ROUTE 1313 AND SEWED ON MAGNETS SO I COULD CLING TO THEIR CARS!
AND I WOULD HAVE GOTTEN AWAY WITH IT, TOO, IF IT WEREN'T FOR THESE MEDDLING KIDS, THEIR DOG, AND THEIR NOISY VAN!
NOW TAKE ME TO JAIL SO I CAN GET SOME PEACE AND QUIET!
ZZZZ!

AND SO...
OOH! NOW I'M AWAKE. DID I MISS ANYTHING?
TERRO
ISLAN
FERR
200
FEET
OH, NOTHING!

WAIT A MINUTE! THE MAGNETS! THE RED SPRAYPAINT! MARTY'S FINGERS!
GUYS! TURN THE VAN AROUND! THERE IS A GREMLIN, AND I KNOW WHO IT IS!
BEWARE
TEXAS
AMERIC

LIKE, FOR ONCE, VELMA, WE'RE WAY AHEAD OF YOU!
?
SCOOBY ROOBY ROOOO!
THE End

HERCULOIDS STAGE SHOW
SOUND STAGE 13
LIKE, GEE, THANKS A LOT!

TODAY'S YOUR LUCKY DAY, SHAGGY. "THE HERCULOIDS" IS ONE OF YOUR FAVORITE SHOWS!
DID YOU GET ZANDOR'S AUTOGRAPH?
NO--

--DIRECTIONS TO THE COMMISSARY!
I'M STARVING!
REE ROO!

LUNCH WILL HAVE TO WAIT. MY GRAMPA TEDDY IS EXPECTING US.
IT SURE WAS NICE OF HIM TO INVITE US TO THE SET WHERE THEY'RE FILMING HIS NEW MOVIE!

HE WANTED TO THANK US FOR THE HELP WE GAVE HIM SOLVING THE MYSTERY OF THE MISSING FILM.*
UH OH, WHAT'S GOING ON OVER THERE?
*SEE SCOOBY-DOO VOL. 1 - YOU MEDDLING KIDS!

RUN FOR YOUR LIVES!
THAT'S GRAMPA TED'S SOUND STAGE! WHAT'S GOING ON?
GHOST!
IT'S A GHOST!
GHOST!
RUN!
SCOOBY-DOO
IN
SOUND STAGE SPOOK
LIKE, NO ONE SAID THIS WAS A SCARY MOVIE!
Writer: JOHN ROZUM
Pencils: JOE STATON
inks: ANDREW PEPOY
letters: JOHN COSTANZA
edits DANA KURTIN
colors: PAUL BECTON

GHOST!
COME ON, GANG, LET'S GO SEE WHAT THIS IS ALL ABOUT!
LIKE, AM I THE ONLY ONE LISTENING? NO WAY I'M GOING IN THERE!
RUH-UH. REE REITHER!

NOT EVEN FOR A COUPLE OF... SCOOBY-SNACKS?
MAKE IT THREE APIECE AND YOU'VE GOT YOURSELF A DEAL!

WORKS EVERY TIME.
WORKS EVERY TIME.

IT'S GREAT TO SEE YOU, GRAMPA TED!
YOU TOO, FREDDY!
... I ONLY WISH IT WERE UNDER BETTER CIRCUMSTANCES.

WHAT'S THIS WE HEARD ABOUT A GHOST?
COME TALK TO TOM BURDEN. HE'S THE PRODUCER AND DIRECTOR OF THE MOVIE!
PLEASE SAY THESE KIDS ARE HERE TO HELP!
DIRECTOR

CLAYTON LONNEY
YOU SEE, THIS IS THE SOUND STAGE WHERE THE LEGENDARY SILENT MOVIE ACTOR CLAYTON LONNEY MADE MOST OF HIS FILMS.
RETROSPECTIVE

NOW HIS GHOST IS MENACING MY CAST AND CREW AND RUINING MY LATEST MASTERPIECE--
NO!
AAA!

--THE GIANT CRUSTACEAN-AT-THE-RACES MOVIE:
"BISQUE, HORROR FROM THE DEEP"!

LIKE, ISN'T THE GIANT-CRUSTACEAN-AT-THE-SPEEDWAY-MOVIE CALLED "CLAWS"?
BITE YOUR TONGUE! THAT'S THE MOVIE LUCAS SPIEGEL IS DIRECTING FOR A RIVAL MOVIE STUDIO!
MINE IS ABOUT A SCARY GIANT CRAB! HIS IS ABOUT A SCARY GIANT LOBSTER! THERE'S NO COMPAR-ISON!

WELL, GANG, SHOWTIME! WE'VE GOT A MYSTERY TO SOLVE.
I WONDER WHY LONNEY IS HAUNTING THIS MOVIE?
I'LL SHOW YOU TODAY'S RUSHES. MAYBE YOU'LL FIND SOME CLUES.

IN THIS SCENE, THE HEROIC SCIENTIST CONFRONTS THE MAD SCIENTIST, PLAYED BY TED.
LIKE, NO POPCORN?
NO RUTROGS? NO RODA? OR CRANDY?

WHY DID YOU BREED A GIANT KING CRAB? WHY?
TO FEED THE WORLD!
MMM... CRABS... WITH BUTTER SAUCE...

MORE LIKE TO FEED ON THE WORLD!
MWA-HA-HA-HA
ZOINKS!
IT'S OKAY, SHAGGY-- IT'S JUST ON THE SCREEN!

MWA HA HA!
ULP THAT LAUGHTER ISN'T COMING FROM THE SCREEN!
NEITHER IS THIS FOG! LOOK!

RUH RHOST!
HA-HA-HA!!!
ZOINKS! IT'S CLAYTON CONNEY!

I'M GETTING OUT OF HERE!
LIKE, DOGS AND CHICKENS FIRST!

??
THE GHOST IS GONE!
HUH?
NO IT ISN'T...

IT'S ON MR. BURDEN'S BACK!
WHAT?!
IT'S JUST A FILM IMAGE! BURDEN BLOCKED THE PROJECTOR, SO THE "GHOST" IS BEING PROJECTED ONTO HIS BACK!

SO THAT'S WHAT THE SMOKE WAS FOR!
WHO EVER IS BEHIND ALL THIS PROJECTED THE "GHOST" ONTO THIS SPECIAL EFFECTS SMOKE TO MAKE IT LOOK LIKE IT WAS FLOATING ON AIR!

LIKE, THEY SHOULD GET AN ACADEMY AWARD-- 'CAUSE THEY WERE SCARIER THAN THAT CRAB!
THAT GIVES ME AN IDEA! C'MON, GANG, EVERYBODY BACK TO THE SOUND STAGE!

FRED, YOU WANTED TO MEET OUR MAKEUP ARTIST, MR. SEVINE. HE'S STUDIED UNDER LONNEY.
FOR ALL THE THANKS I GET.
COULD YOU--
NO! NO WAY!

THAT'S NICK. HE PLAYS THE RACE CAR VILLAIN.
AS IF ANYONE WILL RECOGNIZE ME BEHIND THIS SCAR!
YOU HAVE TO HAVE A SCAR. YOUR CHARACTER'S TERRIBLE ACCIDENT IS WHAT MAKES HIM BECOME A VILLAIN!

I DON'T CARE! I'M NOT WEARING IT UNLESS IT'S MORE ATTRACTIVE!
CLAYTON LONNEY WOULD BE DISGUSTED WITH ACTORS TODAY! IT'S NO WONDER HE'S HAUNTING THIS SET!

WHAT DID YOU KIDS WANT!
... NEVER MIND.

LIKE, THERE'S A GUY WHO NEEDS TO EAT MORE SCOOBY SNACKS!
REAH!
WELL, SO MUCH FOR MY PLAN IN INVOLVING TOM SEVINE, THE MAKE-UP ARTIST! IT ALMOST SOUNDS LIKE HE'S THE GH--
LOOK OUT!
KRASH
THAT WAS CLOSE! MR. JONES, YOU'RE EVEN MORE HEROIC IN REAL LIFE THAN IN YOUR MOVIES! I WONDER WHAT CAUSED THOSE LIGHTS TO FALL?
THERE'S YOUR ANSWER. LOOK UP!
GIANT CRAB CONTROLS
IT'S CLAYTON LONNEY!
GO AFTER HIM, GANG! I'M GOING TO TRY PLAN B!

GEE, SHAGGY, DON'T BE SCARED! THE GHOST IS GONE NOW!
LIKE, I JUST REMEMBERED WHAT SCARES ME ALMOST AS MUCH AS GHOSTS--
--HEIGHTS!
LOOK, EVERYBODY. FOOT-PRINTS!
WHAT KIND OF GHOST LEAVES FOOT-PRINTS?
NOT CLAYTON LONNEY! HE DIED BEFORE THIS TYPE OF SNEAKER EVER EXISTED!
ZOINKS! LIKE, TELL THAT TO HIM!
LET'S GET OUT OF HERE!
THAT'S THE BEST IDEA I'VE HEARD ALL DAY!!
RRRAGGH...
?!
ZOINKS!
IT'S BISQUE-- HORROR FROM THE DEEP!

FRAAAGH!
A CRAB!
RUN RHOST!
WUMP!
FLIP!
AAAAA!
TUMBLE!
SKIDOO
NO!
CUT! THAT'S A WRAP!
SHOOOMP!
YES-- LOOKS LIKE HE'S TIRED OUT!

NICE WORK, KIDS! NOW LET'S SEE WHO THIS "GHOST" IS.

IT'S LUCAS SPIEGEL, THE DIRECTOR OF "CLAWS"!
THE OTHER GIANT CRAB MOVIE?
"LOBSTER!" IT'S A LOBSTER!

MR. SPIEGEL WAS TRYING TO STOP YOUR MOVIE SO THAT HIS WOULD MAKE IT INTO THE THEATERS FIRST!
ONLY A DIRECTOR WITH HIS SPECIAL EFFECTS KNOWHOW COULD HAVE CREATED THAT "GHOST" IN THE FOG IN THE SCREENING ROOM!

THAT'S RIGHT!
AND I WOULD HAVE GOTTEN AWAY WITH IT TOO, IF IT WEREN'T FOR THOSE MEDDLING KIDS AND THAT LAME GIANT CRAB WHICH ISN'T EVEN CLOSE TO BEING AS COOL AS MY GIANT LOBSTER!

LIKE, I'M GLAD WE SOLVED THE MYSTERY--
RAAR!
--BECAUSE WE'RE GONNA BE CRUSTACEAN KIBBLE!
ROOK ROUT!

DON'T BE SILLY, SHAGGY. DIDN'T YOU RECOGNIZE THE CRAB'S VOICE?
RAAAGH! GRR!
GIANT CRAB CONTROLS

SO THAT WAS "PLAN B", FRED! YOU WERE GOING TO USE THE GIANT CRAB TO SCARE THE TRUTH OUT OF THE "GHOST"!
IT WORKED PRETTY WELL ON SHAG AND SCOOB, TOO!

GOOD GOING, FREDERICK! I SEE YOU INHERITED MY LOOKS, MY FASHION SENSE, AND MY ACTING ABILITY!
THANKS, GRAMPA TED!
THAT'S IT!

YOU KIDS HAVE GIVEN ME A GREAT IDEA FOR MY NEXT MOVIE! WHAT DO YOU THINK?
SOUND STAGE SPOOK

HA HA HA HA
AS LONG AS THERE'S POPCORN, I'M THERE!
RAND ROTROGS. SLUURP!
THE END

EGYPT...
AT LAST! I'VE FOUND IT!

WHAT DOES IT SAY?
IT'S AN ANCIENT CURSE. "WHOEVER DEFILES THE TOMB OF KHUFU SHALL RELEASE THE DEADLY SPIRIT OF THE DESERT."

OF COURSE, IT'S JUST ANCIENT SUPER-STITION, MEANT TO FRIGHTEN AWAY THIEVES.
I CAN'T WAIT TO SHOW ALL THIS TO MY COLLEAGUES BACK AT THE UNIVERSITY!
PROFESSOR ...DID YOU HEAR SOMETHING?

HSSSS
I HEARD IT AGAIN!
IT'S PROBABLY JUST SHIFTING SAND, HABIB. WHAT COULD POSSIBLY HURT US DOWN HERE?

The CURSE of the SCARY SCARAB
writer: JESSE LEON McCANN
Pencils: JOE STATON
inks: ANDREW PEPOY
letters: JOHN COSTANZA
colors: PAUL BECTON
edits: DANA KURTIN
HISSSS
GOOD HEAVENS!
YIIIEE!

SEVERAL WEEKS LATER...
HERE WE ARE, GANG! THE CAIRO AIRPORT!
CAIRO

munch! ALREADY, FRED? BUT LIKE, WE HAVEN'T FINISHED OUR COMPLIMENTARY PEANUTS AND PRETZELS! chomp!
BESIDES, I THINK THE FLIGHT ATTENDANTS ARE GONNA MISS US! RIGHT, SCOOB?
REAH, REAH! REANUTS!
NEXT TIME THE DOG RIDES IN THE CARGO HOLD!
NEXT TIME, THEY BOTH RIDE IN THE CARGO HOLD!

LET'S NOT FORGET WHY WE CAME TO EGYPT IN THE FIRST PLACE!
TELEGRAM
TO: NORVILLE "SHAGGY" ROGERS
FROM: THE EGYPTIAN GOVERNMENT
WE REGRET TO INFORM YOU THAT PROF. HENRY ROGERS IS MISSING FROM HIS LATEST DIG AND IS PRESUMED LOST. PLEASE COME TO CAIRO A.S.A.P. FOR THE READING OF THE WILL. THE LAWYER BEN ABI WILL MEET YOU AT THE AIRPORT.

GOSH, SHAGGY, I NEVER KNEW YOUR GREAT UNCLE WAS SUCH A FAMOUS ARCHAEOLOGIST!
THE TELEGRAM SAYS THEY'RE READING HIS WILL IN THE TOMBS HE FOUND ON HIS LATEST DIG!
JINKIES! LISTEN TO THIS, GANG!
ALSO IN THIS SERIES: HAUNTED HOUSES
ANCIENT TOMBS

"THE CRYPTS OF PHARAOHS WERE OFTEN CURSED, THREATENING POTENTIAL GRAVE-ROBBERS WITH SICKNESS, OR EVEN DEATH!"
D-D-DEATH? LIKE, THAT'S MY LEAST FAVORITE TYPE OF CURSE!
RE, ROO!
PRETZELS
PEANUTS

MAYBE WE SHOULD JUST CATCH THE NEXT FLIGHT OUTTA TOWN!
ROOD RIDEA!
DON'T BE SUCH SCAREDY-CATS, YOU TWO!
GREETINGS! I AM BEN ABI, EXECUTOR OF THE PROFESSOR'S WILL. MY CAR IS JUST OUTSIDE.

I MUST WARN YOU THAT MYSTERIOUS GOINGS-ON AT THE DIGGING SITE HAVE FRIGHTENED AWAY ALL OF THE WORKERS.
THEY CLAIM THE PLACE IS CURSED BY AN ANCIENT GIANT COBRA.
ZOINKS! GIANT COBRA?!

COME ON, GUYS! YOU AREN'T SCARED OF AN OLD SNAKE CURSE, ARE YOU?
LIKE, IS THAT A TRICK QUESTION?!

JOINING US FOR THE READING OF THE WILL ARE PROF. ROGERS' TWO REMAINING ASSISTANTS, OMAR AND KHYYAM, FROM THE UNIVERSITY.
WOW! IS THIS PLACE WILD OR WHAT?
I PICK "OR WHAT"!
IT'S BEAUTIFUL!

"TO MY GREAT-NEPHEW SHAGGY, I LEAVE THE PRICELESS RUBY SCARAB BEETLE I FOUND IN THESE TOMBS, A TREASURE FIT FOR A PHARAOH!"
LIKE, I'M GONNA PUT IT ON DISPLAY. PRICE OF ADMISSION--ONE DOZEN HAMBURGERS!
REAH! REAH!

OMAR AND KHYYAM WILL EACH RECEIVE A FELLOWSHIP GRANT AT CAIRO UNIVERSITY SO THEY MAY CONTINUE THEIR STUDIES.
HOW GENEROUS OF THE PRO-FESSOR.
WE ARE MOST APPRECIA-TIVE.

I DON'T KNOW WHO'S MORE OF A STONE-FACE, THESE OLD CARVINGS OR THOSE TWO ASSISTANTS!
NOW IT IS TIME FOR SHAGGY TO RECEIVE THE SCARAB.

LADIES AND GENTLEMEN, THE PRICELESS SCARAB OF KING KHUFU!
OH, IT'S STUNNING!
HSSSSSSSSS!
LIKE, DO YOU GUYS HEAR SOME-THING?

HEY!
ZOINKS! LIKE, WHAT HAPPENED TO THE LIGHTS?!
HSSSSSSSSSS

AAAAAAA!
THAT'S MR. ABI!

JINKIES! MR. ABI IS GONE!
AND SO'S THE SCARAB!
LIKE, GOOD IDEA! ME FIRST!
REE RIRST!
HANG ON, YOU TWO! LOOKS LIKE WE'VE GOT A MYSTERY TO SOLVE!

AND I THINK I'VE DISCOVERED OUR FIRST CLUE!
THESE TRACKS WERE MADE BY A MEMBER OF THE COBRA FAMILY. BUT THEY'RE HUGE! THIS SNAKE MUST BE 12 FEET LONG!

HMM! THE SNAKE TRACKS GO RIGHT PAST WHERE MR. ABI WAS STANDING--AND THEN INTO THE TOMBS!
JEEPERS! YOU MEAN THE SNAKE ATE MR. ABI?

C'MON, GANG! WE'VE GOT A MAP OF THE TOMBS. LET'S SEE IF WE CAN GET TO THE BOTTOM OF THIS AND GET SHAGGY'S SCARAB BACK.
OH, DON'T BOTHER ON MY ACCOUNT!
LET'S GO, YOU TWO CHICKENS!

THAT'S RIGHT! LIKE, NO ONE HERE BUT US CHICKENS! CLUCK! CLUCK!
...
ROCK-A-DOOBY-DOO!

THAT'S STRANGE! WE'VE REACHED A DEAD END!
FRED, DO YOU HAVE TO USE THAT TERM?
THE SNAKE TRACKS VANISH WHEN THEY REACH THAT WALL. CURIOUSER AND CURIOUSER!

MAYBE WE SHOULD GO BACK AND REPORT THIS TO THE AUTHORITIES.
LIKE, THAT'S THE BEST IDEA I'VE HEARD ALL DAY!
I WONDER IF SNAKES CAN CLIMB WALLS?

ZOINKS! DAPHNE'S DISAPPEARED!
ROH, NO! RAPHNE!

RELAX, EVERYONE! LEAVE IT TO DANGER-PRONE DAPHNE TO FIND A SECRET PASSAGEWAY!
SO, LIKE, SHE JUST TRIPPED IN THE CRYPT!
OOOPS!

LET'S SPLIT UP. SHAGGY, YOU AND SCOOBY FOLLOW THE SNAKE TRACKS. THE REST OF US WILL FOLLOW THESE FOOTPRINTS.
LIKE, HOW DID I KNOW YOU WERE GONNA SAY THAT?! NO WAY! UH-UH! I AM NOT FOLLOWING ANY OLD GIANT COBRA!

WILL YOU DO IT FOR A--SCOOBY SNACK?

AT LEAST THIS TIME WE GOT THE JUMBO SIZE.
RUM-MY!

LOOK, SCOOB!
CATS WERE TREATED LIKE ROYALTY IN ANCIENT EGYPT.
ROH, BLECHH!

LIKE, DON'T BE BLUE, SCOOBY-DOO!
DOGS WERE TREATED WELL, TOO!
REE-HEE-HEE!

OH, GREAT! THE SNAKE TRACKS GO EVERY WHICH-A-WAY!
BUT, LIKE, WHICH-A-WAY DO WE GO?
HSSSSS
RULP! ROT RAT RAY!

HSSSSS
RUN, SCOOB, RUN!
REEELP!

LIKE, WE MADE IT, SCOOB!
SLAM!

RAGGY, ROOK! RITCHEN!
WELL, WHADDAYA KNOW? THE SNAKE CHASED US TO THE SNACKS! WHAT'S ALL THIS FOOD DOING IN AN OLD TOMB?
OH WELL, I'LL MAKE THE SANDWICHES. YOU GET THE MUSTARD, PICKLES AND JELLY!

ROKAY!
RICKLES
RUNIONS
RELLY
RUSTARD
RUMMIES...

RUMMIES?!

REEELP!
LIKE, I WANT MY MOMMY, NOT A MUMMY!
C'MON, DOOR! OPEN SESAME!
MMMPHHH! MMMMPH!

GRRRR!
ZOINKS! LIKE, CLOSE, SESAME!

WHICH WAY?!
SCARY HOODED GUYS...
MUMMIES...

LIKE, SORRY, HOODED GUYS--
--YOU WIN!
GANGWAY!
OOF!

WOW! A WORKSHOP-- IN A TOMB?
WHY WOULD AN ARCHAEOLOGICAL TEAM NEED ALL THIS? IT LOOKS LIKE THEY WERE BUILDING SOMETHING IN HERE!
OR TAKING A TRIP! LOOK AT THAT SUITCASE!

GOOD GOING, DAPHNE! WE'VE FOUND THE SCARAB!
AND CHECK THIS OUT--

I THINK I'VE FIGURED OUT THIS MYSTERY!
HSSSSSSS

HSSSSSSSSSSSS
THE COBRA!
WE'RE TRAPPED!!
IT CAN'T GET US ALL AT ONCE! KEEP MOVING!

LIKE, AAAAAA!
GRRRRRR!
MMMPH!

QUICK, SCOOB! HIDE IN THIS URN!
ROO ROT RIT!
ZIPP!

LIKE, HUH?? THIS IS EITHER ANOTHER SECRET PASSAGEWAY--
--OR THE BIGGEST URN IN HISTORY!
RIIKES!
SLIIIDE!

DOUBLE "YIKES!"
KRUNCH
SHAG? SCOOB?

HISSS-HIC-HISSS-REORWER-SSSSS!
FRED! VELMA! RUN!
CRACKLE!
SPARK!
IT'S OKAY, SHAGGY! THE SNAKE'S JUST A ROBOT!

YEAH, BUT *THOSE* TWO ARE *REAL*!
KRKLE... SMK...

AAH!
LOOK OUT!

THEY'RE REAL, ALL RIGHT--REAL *DOWN*!
TALK ABOUT BEING IN THE WRONG PLACE AT THE WRONG TIME--
--THE COMPUTERIZED COBRA CAUGHT THEM COMPLETELY!
WHAM!

MMMMMPH!
WUMPH!
ZOINKS! WE FORGOT ALL ABOUT THE MUMMIES!

THESE AREN'T MUMMIES! IT'S MR. ABI AND YOUR GREAT-UNCLE PROFESSOR ROGERS!
Gasp! THOSE BLACK-HOODED MEN CAPTURED US, TIED US UP IN SURGICAL BANDAGES AND LOCKED US IN THE PANTRY!

OMAR AND KHYYAM? YOU DID THIS!
YES! THEY BUILT A GIANT MECHANICAL COBRA TO SCARE EVERY-ONE OFF AND STEAL THE SCARAB!
AND WE WOULD HAVE GOTTEN AWAY WITH IT, TOO, IF IT WEREN'T FOR THE EGYPTIAN GOVERNMENT CALLING IN THESE MEDDLING KIDS!

DEAR GRAND-NEPHEW SHAGGY! I'M SO SORRY TO HAVE PUT YOU THROUGH ALL THIS! AND I'M AFRAID NOW THE SCARAB MUST GO TO A MUSEUM.
OH, LIKE, THAT'S OKAY, UNCLE HENRY. I KNOW A CERTAIN HOODED DUO'S PANTRY NEARBY FULL OF SANDWICHES THAT'LL MAKE UP FOR IT! RIGHT, SCOOB?

RO RUMMIES, ROKAY? RUST RUSTARD!
YOU GOT IT!
THE END

IT WAS REALLY GENEROUS TO BRING US TO ENGLAND WITH YOU, CECELIA.
NONSENSE, DAPHNE. I'VE LIVED NEXT TO SHAGGY'S PARENTS SINCE HE WAS A BOY.
SPEAKING OF ME, LIKE, LET'S GET SOME ENGLISH CHOW!
REAH, REAH!
EXCHA

I'M STARVED!
NOT SO FAST, MY LAD!
YOUR MOTHER TOLD ME YOU'D PROTECT ME FROM CHEATS AND CHAR-LATANS!

PSYCHIC FAIR
Bath, England
AS IF I COULDN'T TELL THE DIFFERENCE BETWEEN REAL PSYCHICS AND FAKES!
RUH-OH!
FORTUNE
Psychic Psyche-Out!
JOE EDKIN WRITER
JOHN DELANEY PENCILS
DAVE COOPER INKS
JOHN COSTANZA LETTERS
PAUL BECTON COLORS
DANA KURTIN EDITS

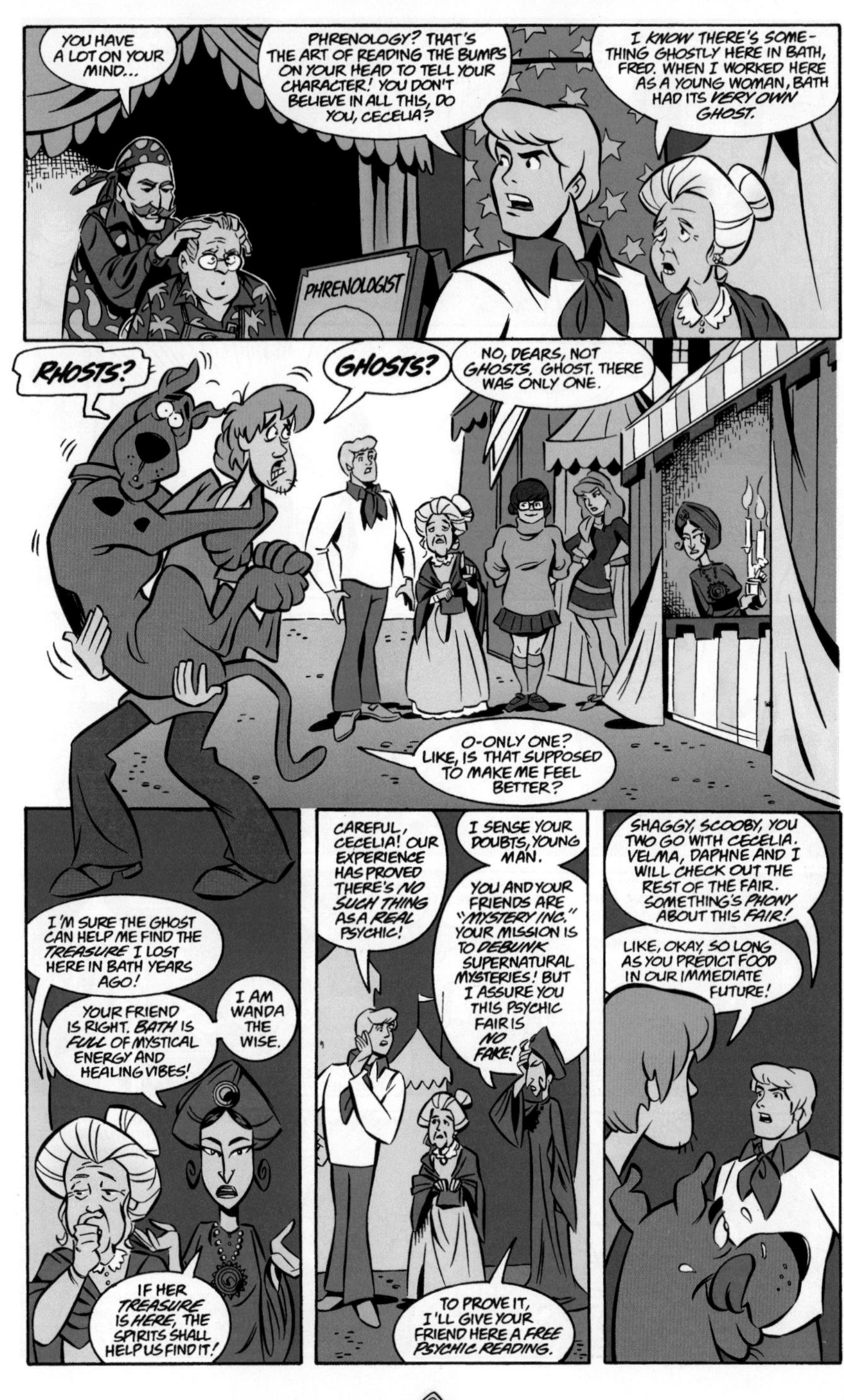
YOU HAVE A LOT ON YOUR MIND...
PHRENOLOGY? THAT'S THE ART OF READING THE BUMPS ON YOUR HEAD TO TELL YOUR CHARACTER! YOU DON'T BELIEVE IN ALL THIS, DO YOU, CECELIA?
PHRENOLOGIST
I KNOW THERE'S SOMETHING GHOSTLY HERE IN BATH, FRED. WHEN I WORKED HERE AS A YOUNG WOMAN, BATH HAD ITS VERY OWN GHOST.
RHOSTS?
GHOSTS?
NO, DEARS, NOT GHOSTS. GHOST. THERE WAS ONLY ONE.
O-ONLY ONE? LIKE, IS THAT SUPPOSED TO MAKE ME FEEL BETTER?
I'M SURE THE GHOST CAN HELP ME FIND THE TREASURE I LOST HERE IN BATH YEARS AGO!
I AM WANDA THE WISE.
YOUR FRIEND IS RIGHT. BATH IS FULL OF MYSTICAL ENERGY AND HEALING VIBES!
IF HER TREASURE IS HERE, THE SPIRITS SHALL HELP US FIND IT!
CAREFUL, CECELIA! OUR EXPERIENCE HAS PROVED THERE'S NO SUCH THING AS A REAL PSYCHIC!
I SENSE YOUR DOUBTS, YOUNG MAN.
YOU AND YOUR FRIENDS ARE "MYSTERY INC." YOUR MISSION IS TO DEBUNK SUPERNATURAL MYSTERIES! BUT I ASSURE YOU THIS PSYCHIC FAIR IS NO FAKE!
TO PROVE IT, I'LL GIVE YOUR FRIEND HERE A FREE PSYCHIC READING.
SHAGGY, SCOOBY, YOU TWO GO WITH CECELIA. VELMA, DAPHNE AND I WILL CHECK OUT THE REST OF THE FAIR. SOMETHING'S PHONY ABOUT THIS FAIR!
LIKE, OKAY, SO LONG AS YOU PREDICT FOOD IN OUR IMMEDIATE FUTURE!

YOU LIVE ON FAIRCHESTER LANE...
WHY, THAT'S RIGHT!
GHOST METER
THAT MIND READER HAS A PHONE BOOK IN HER LAP TO LOOK UP PEOPLE'S ADDRESSES!

YOUR FUTURE IS VERY BRIGHT...
NOT AS BRIGHT AS HER HIDDEN SUN LAMP!

GERARD'S SPIRIT IS HOLDING THE CANDLE!
GEE, I DIDN'T KNOW SPIRITS KNEW HOW TO USE PIANO WIRE!
I HOPE CECELIA'S NOT FALLING FOR A SCAM LIKE THIS!

THE KEY TO FINDING YOUR TREASURE IS IN YOUR OWN MIND.
THE GHOST OF BATH WILL GUIDE YOU.
HOW TRUE, DEAR!
LIKE, HUH?!
I'LL JOG MY MEMORY BY VISITING WHERE I WORKED WHEN I LIVED HERE!
PIES

RHOST OF RATH?!
ZOINKS!
DON'T WORRY ABOUT IT, GUYS.
THERE'S NOTHING SUPERNATURAL HERE-- THIS FAIR IS A FRAUD!
YOU'LL REGRET SAYING THAT! THE GHOST OF BATH WILL TEACH YOU A LESSON!

WE'RE SORRY IF YOU'RE DISAPPOINTED, CECELIA.
NOT AT ALL, DEAR! THAT FORTUNE TELLER GAVE ME VERY GOOD ADVICE. I HAVE TO VISIT--

--THE SUSIE LYNN HOUSE! I WORKED HERE AS A YOUNG WOMAN MAKING "SUSIE LYNN" BUNS!
LIKE, THIS CASE IS LOOKING UP! WE CAN EAT AND LOOK FOR CLUES!
I WARN YOU-- IF YOU GO IN THERE, YOU WILL FACE GREAT DANGER!

ANOTHER WACKY PSYCHIC PREDICTION?
I DON'T REMEMBER SEEING HIS BOOTH AT THE FAIR.
IT DOESN'T SEEM TO HAVE STOPPED SHAG AND SCOOB...

NOTHING HERE LOOKS DANGEROUS TO ME!
RUH-UH!
STEAK AND KIDNEY PIE, COTTAGE PIE, SCONES WITH CLOTTED CREAM, PLOUGHMAN'S LUNCH, CORNISH PASTIE, WATERCRESS SAND-WICHES, AND JELLIED EELS...

REEEEE-LICIOUS!
I'M STUFFED!
I CAN'T BELIEVE YOU ATE ALL THAT. JELLIED EELS AND CLOTTED CREAM? ICK!

HAVE YOU REMEMBERED ANYTHING, CECELIA?
YES! SUSIE LYNN'S ORIGINAL KITCHEN IS STILL IN THE BASEMENT. SINCE THAT'S WHERE THE GHOST LIVES...
...MAYBE THE GHOST CAN HELP ME REMEMBER WHERE I LEFT MY TREASURE!
SHOULDN'T SOMEONE STAY UP HERE AND GUARD THE FOOD?
C'MON, GUYS. HOW ABOUT A--
--SCOOBY SNACK?
ROOBY RACKS! REAH!
I GUESS THERE'S ALWAYS ROOM FOR SCOOBY SNACKS!
GIFTS
IT'S A GIFT SHOP NOW, BUT THIS HEARTH IS WHERE SUSIE LYNN FIRST BAKED HER WORLD-FAMOUS BREADS...
GASP! THAT'S IT!
THAT FORTUNE-TELLER WAS RIGHT! I DO REMEMBER!
I HID MY TREASURE UNDER THIS FLAG-STONE!

C'MON, SHAGGY, PUT YOUR BACK INTO IT!
LIKE, I'M TRYING, BUT MY STOMACH'S IN THE WAY!
GOT IT!
I AM SUSIE LYNN, THE GHOST OF BATH--
--AND THAT BOX IS MINE!
RETURN THE TREASURE TO ME AND I SHALL SPARE YOUR LIVES!
THAT SMOKE--!
COUGH! COUGH! LET'S GET OUT OF HERE, GUYS!
HURRY, CECELIA!
BUT, DEAR--
COME ON! SHE WANTS YOUR TREASURE!
MINE!
YOU'LL NEVER ESCAPE! RETURN THE TREASURE!
WHICH WAY NOW?
LIKE, DOES IT MATTER?
GANGWAY!

STAY NEAR ME, CECELIA!
BUT--
THAT TREASURE BELONGS TO ME!

GIVE IT BACK!
VELMA! CATCH!

FLING!
IT'S GOOD!

DAPHNE! DOUBLE BLUFF RIGHT!
GOT IT!

SHAGGY! SCOOBY! IT'S UP TO YOU!
PUNT
IT'S ALL UP TO THE KID FROM COOLSVILLE!

--AND HE FUMBLES!
GRAB IT, SCOOB!
RHY'M RYING!
KA-WHUMP!
HAHAHAH
ZOINKS!
THAT WAS ONE VICIOUS TACKLE!

ARE YOU OKAY, MY DEARS?
REAH.
LIKE, SUSIE IS PRETTY SOLID FOR A GHOST.
PLUS SHE'S GOT SOME GNARLY DANDRUFF!

THAT'S NOT DANDRUFF, SHAGGY-- THAT'S FLOUR!
"SUSIE LYNN" WAS NO GHOST.
AND THIS NECKLACE SHE LEFT BEHIND WILL LEAD US RIGHT TO THE IMPOSTOR!

WHAT? I'M CLOSED--
OH, IT'S YOU! COME FOR ANOTHER READING?

THERE'S OUR "GHOST," GUYS! WANDA THE WISE!
I HAVE NO IDEA WHAT YOU'RE TALKING ABOUT!
NO? THEN HOW DID YOU GET--

--CECELIA'S BOX?
I'VE NEVER SEEN THIS BEFORE IN MY LIFE!
PERHAPS THE GHOST OF BATH WANTED ME TO HAVE IT AND LEFT IT HERE!

AND DEAR ME, HERE'S YOUR SWEET GHOSTLY COSTUME!
BUT YOU DIDN'T DO YOUR RESEARCH, DUCKIE. THE GHOST OF BATH ISN'T SUSIE LYNN--
--BUT HER OLD CAT SNIFFLES!

THERE IS NO GHOST OF BATH! IT WAS YOU ALL ALONG!
YOU LOST YOUR NECKLACE IN THE SCUFFLE. YOU TRIED TO FOOL US WITH GHOSTLY "FLOUR" SMOKE, WHICH IS STILL ON YOUR CLOTHES--
--AND ON YOUR FOOT-PRINTS WHICH LED US RIGHT BACK TO YOUR TENT!

WHAT?
WELL, I TRIED TO TELL YOU, DEARS, BUT YOU WOULDN'T LISTEN.
RHOST RAT? RO ROTHER...

PARDON--I'M INSPECTOR MORRIS OF THE BATH POLICE. I'VE BEEN FOLLOWING THIS FAIR FOR MONTHS TRYING TO UNCOVER THEIR SCAMS.
IS THERE A PROBLEM HERE?
WANDA THE WISE IS RUNNING A CROOKED PSYCHIC FAIR AND TRIED TO STEAL CECELIA FOGBOTTOM'S TREASURE.
DID SHE? AND WHY IS THAT?

THE FAIR IS NEARLY BROKE--I FIGURED IF I COULD FOOL YOU KIDS, THE PUBLICITY WOULD HELP BUSINESS AND THE MONEY FROM THE TREASURE WOULD PAY OFF OUR DEBTS!
MAYBE YOU'D GET MORE BUSINESS IF YOU TOLD PEOPLE FORTUNE TELLING IS FOR FUN, NOT FOR FATE.
BESIDES--MY TREASURE IS VALU-ABLE ONLY TO ME.
THEY'RE MY MOTHER'S OLD RECIPES!

THAT'S TREASURE ENOUGH FOR ME! LET'S EAT!
I THOUGHT YOU JUST ATE, DEAR!
LIKE, THAT WAS TEN MINUTES AGO!

BUT, LIKE, ONE QUESTION, INSPECTOR MORRIS--HOW DID YOU KNOW WE'D FACE DANGER IF WE WENT INTO THE RESTAURANT? ARE YOU PSYCHIC?
HEAVENS NO!
ANYONE WHO GOES INTO SUSIE LYNN'S IS IN DANGER OF OVEREATING. THE FOOD'S TOO GOOD!
RHY'LL RAY! ROOBY ROOBY ROOOO!
The End

RACEWAY
JOHNNY, THANKS FOR THE HELP IN FIXING THE MYSTERY MACHINE!
GOOD THING DAPHNE'S COUSIN IS A FAMOUS RACE-CAR DRIVER!
WITH A GREAT MECHANIC!
AW, SHUCKS.
RACE-CAR DRIVING, LIKE, THAT'S THE GROOVIEST. WHERE DO I SIGN UP?
VROOM! VROOM! HEE HEE HEE!
THE MYSTERY MACHINE
GLAD TO HELP OUT. SPARKY'S BEEN ITCHING FOR SOMETHING TO DO ANYHOW, SINCE I'VE STOPPED RACING.
WHAT?
YOU'RE KIDDING, RIGHT?
RHUT?
I WISH! BUT--
--I HAVE TO QUIT. BECAUSE OF THE GHOST!
GHOST?
LIKE, MAYBE I DON'T WANT TO BE A DRIVER AFTER ALL!
WRAITHCAR DRIVER
WRITER: JOHN ROZUM
PENCILS: RURIK TYLER
INKS: DAN DAVIS
LETTERS: JOHN COSTANZA
ASSISTS: HARVEY RICHARDS
EDITS: DANA KURTIN

YES, GHOST!
THE LAST TIME I TOOK MY CAR FOR A FEW TEST LAPS AROUND THE TRACK...

"...Suddenly this second car came out of nowhere!"
HA HA HA!

"The driver was steering into me--
SLAM!
--"trying to force me off the track and crash!"

SCREEEEE!
"I lost control of my car--

"--and crashed into the hay bales along the track!
"I only got a few bruises, but my racer was RUINED...
"And the ghost was gone! But I KNEW him instantly--"

--IT'S AXEL MALONE, THE WORLD'S BEST DRIVER!
OR HE *WAS*--UNTIL HE WAS *KILLED* IN A FREAK CRASH IN LAST YEAR'S FORTUNE *500*.

HIS GHOST'S CRASHED THREE OF THE OTHER TOP DRIVERS. THE FORTUNE *500*'S NEXT WEEK--BUT ALL FOUR OF US HAVE DROPPED OUT.
SMITH OUT
JONES OUT
DOE OUT

LIKE, *DEFINITELY* COUNT ME *OUT* OF THIS RACING GROOVE!
ASK FRED, I DON'T EVEN *LIKE* DRIVING!
REE REITHER!

WITH ALL THOSE DRIVERS OUT, WHO'S LEFT TO RACE?
ALL THE *NEW* DRIVERS. THE BEST BET IS A GUY NAMED CARL VEGA.
SPEAKING OF VEGA--

--LOOK WHO JUST PULLED UP ON THE OTHER SIDE OF THE TRACK!
COME ON, GANG. LET'S GO PAY HIM A VISIT.
YOU DO THAT. WE'LL BE HERE WORKING ON THE *'MACHINE!'*

GHOST?
I HAVEN'T SEEN ANY GHOST.
EVEN IF I DID, THE FORTUNE 500 IS THE BIGGEST RACE OF THE YEAR. NOTHING'S GOING TO SCARE ME OFF!
WATCH AND YOU'LL SEE WHAT THOSE OTHER DRIVERS ARE REALLY AFRAID OF...
...ME WINNING!
15
WHAT A HOT DOGGER!
ZOOOOOOM!!!
COULD CARL VEGA BE THE GHOST...?
JINKIES, HE SURE IS FAST.
LIKE, SO'S WHOEVER'S DRIVING THAT OTHER CAR.

THE GHOST!
VROOOM
OH, NO! CARL, LOOK OUT!
CRASH!
HE'S OUT OF CONTROL!
SQUEAL!

JINKIES! HE'S CRASHED!
FIRE
KER-SMASH

THAT CREEPY CAR VANISHED INTO THIN AIR!
ULP! LIKE, THAT'S HOW I LIKE MY CREEPY CARS!
FIRE
HURRY, GANG! LET'S MAKE SURE CARL'S ALL RIGHT!

CARL, ARE YOU OKAY? SHOULD I CALL AN AMBULANCE?
NO, I'M JUST A BIT SHAKY.

LOOKS LIKE I WON'T BE RACING IN THE FORTUNE 500 AFTER ALL.
I DIDN'T BELIEVE YOU BEFORE, BUT NOW I'M OUT! EVEN IF MY CAR WEREN'T WRECKED, I'M NOT RACING AGAINST THAT GHOST!

WE HAVE TO SOLVE THIS MYSTERY.
JOHNNY AND THE OTHER RACERS ARE DEPENDING ON US!
GOOD LUCK, DAPHNE. LET US KNOW HOW IT TURNS OUT!

WILL YOU STAY--
--FOR A SCOOBY SNACK?
SCOOBY SNAX
LIKE, DRAT! YOU'VE FOUND OUR WEAKNESS!

LET'S TALK TO JOHNNY AND GET SOME...
...CLUES?
NOBODY'S HERE.
JOHNNY ZOOM--
--WHERE ARE YOU?

LIKE, LET'S CHECK THE CON-CESSION STAND!
REAH!
LIKE, THAT WAY WE CAN SOLVE THE MYSTERY OF WHAT'S FOR LUNCH! HOO-HOO
SCOOBY SNACK

YOU DON'T THINK JOHNNY ZOOM OR SPARKY COULD BE THE GHOST, DO YOU, FRED?
IT'S THE ONLY LEAD WE HAVE SO FAR...
LOOK! I'VE JUST FOUND ANOTHER.

WHAT IS IT, VELMA?
WELL, THIS SET OF TIRE TRACKS IS FROM AXEL'S CAR.
SO, THESE TRACKS MUST BE FROM THE GHOST CAR.

AND LOOK! THEY VANISH RIGHT HERE!

HEY, SCOOB--
--WILL YOU MOVE THAT TOOL BOX, SO WE CAN LOOK AT THE TRACK BY THAT WALL?
TOO BAD IT'S NOT A LUNCH BOX. I'M STARVED!
FLIP!
RIKES!
ZOINKS!
NICE JOB, SCOOBY! IT LOOKS LIKE YOU FOUND A SECRET DOOR IN THE RACETRACK WALL!
:ULP: LIKE, I'VE HEARD OF A SKELETON KEY, BUT A SKELETON WRENCH?
IT'S A SECRET GARAGE--
--WITH PICTURES OF AXEL MALONE AND HIS CAR EVERY-WHERE!

LIKE, CAN'T WE LEAVE IT A SECRET?
AND LOOK AT ALL THESE CANS OF PAINT-- THE SAME COLORS AS THE GHOST CAR. ENOUGH TO PAINT TWO CARS!
SNIFF! SNIFF!

RIKES!
RH-RHOST!
WHERE? WHERE?

RELAX, YOU TWO.
ONLY GHOST PEOPLE WEAR SHEETS-- NOT GHOST CARS.
ZOINKS! SO MUCH FOR THAT THEORY, FRED!
RAAAALP!
VROOOOOOM!
WE HAVE TO GO AFTER HIM!
WE DO?
HOW? CARL VEGA'S CAR IS WRECKED, AND JOHNNY ZOOM'S IS UP ON BLOCKS.
RE RHOO?
THE MYSTERY MACHINE!
IT'S NEVER FAILED US YET!

LIKE, YOU'RE GOING THE WRONG WAY, FRED. THE EXIT'S BACK THERE!
I WAS AFRAID YOU'D SAY THAT. GULP
WE'RE NOT LEAVING UNTIL WE CATCH THAT GHOST!

HURRY, FRED, HE'S GAINING ON US!
I THOUGHT WE WERE SUPPOSED TO BE CHASING HIM!

OH NO!
OIL
SPARKY DIDN'T FINISH FIXING THE MYSTERY MACHINE!

WE'RE STILL LEAKING OIL!
VROOM

JINKIES!
THE GHOST CAR HIT THE OIL!
IT'S SPINNING OUT OF CONTROL!
THE MYSTERY MACHINE
SCREEE!

SKRASH!
HURRY! IF HE'S NOT A GHOST, HE'LL NEED OUR HELP!

THE GHOST CAR--CRASHED?!
I'LL TAKE CARE OF THE FIRE. YOU GUYS NAB THAT GHOST!
WE'RE ON IT!
IT'S STANLEY TESTAROSA--THE BIGGEST LONG SHOT IN THE FORTUNE 500!

NOW THAT YOU'RE SAFE, LET'S SEE WHO YOU REALLY ARE!
HE WAS TRYING TO SCARE EVERYONE OUT OF THE RACE SO HE'D WIN!
THAT'S WHY HE BECAME THE "GHOST" OF AXEL MALONE AND BUILT A SECRET GARAGE IN THE TRACK!
OUR BIGGEST CLUE WAS THOSE EXTRA CANS OF PAINT FOR RESTORING HIS CAR AFTER EVERY CRASH!
AND I WOULD HAVE GOTTEN AWAY WITH IT TOO, IF IT WEREN'T FOR YOU MEDDLING KIDS.

THERE'S JUST ONE THING I WANT TO KNOW, JOHNNY-- WHERE WERE YOU TWO THIS WHOLE TIME?
OH, SPARKY AND I WENT DOWN TO THE CONCESSION STAND TO GRAB SOME LUNCH, SINCE SHAG AND SCOOB ATE ALL OF OURS.

SPEAKING OF SHAGGY AND SCOOBY, WHERE ARE THEY?
I DON'T THINK IT'S ANY MYSTERY WHERE THEY'VE GONE!

RUM-MY!
LIKE, THE CARS AREN'T THE ONLY THINGS AROUND HERE THAT NEED RE-FUELLING!

HA HA HA HA HA
ROOBY RACER ROO!
THE End

AHHHH, THIS IS THE LIFE!
GOOD FOOD, GOOD FRIENDS, AND BEST OF ALL--NO MYSTERIES!
RUH-HUH!
GROOVY! OUR CAJUN-STYLE, ANCHOVY, CURRY, GARLIC, AND ONION PIZZA HAS ARRIVED!
I SHOULD HAVE KNOWN YOU TWO ORDERED THIS STINKER!
PIZZA
RIZZA! REAH, REAH!
PEE-YEW! WHAD HAVE YOU BEEN EADING? YOU ZDINK!
YOU DWO NEED A BATH!
RATH?!
MUNCH! MUNCH! SORRY, VELMA, CAN'T HEAR YOU--EATING!
SAY, VELMA, YOU SOUND LIKE YOU'RE COMIN' DOWN WITH A COLD.
MAYBE SOME GARLIC WOULD HELP.
TROUBLE, GANG.
PHEW! WHAT DIED IN HERE?
SOMEONE--OR TWO!--NEEDS A BATH!
CAN'T HEAR YOU,FRED! EATING!
ANYHOW, YOU GUYS'LL NEVER BELIEVE WHAT I UNCOVERED FILLING UP THE MYSTERY MACHINE AT BIG RALPH'S CAR WASH--

GHOST in the Machina
--A MYSTERY!
WRITER: TERRANCE GRIEP
PENCILS: JOE STATON
INKS: ANDREW PEPOY
LETTERS: JOHN COSTANZA
COLORS: PAUL BECTON
EDITS: DANA KURTIN
RO BOY. RI RELIEVE RIT.
ME TOO, LOU.
ZO AFTER SHAG AND ZCOOB DAKE A BATH, WE--
LIKE, HAVE YOU FLIPPED, FRED?
THERE'S A CASE NEEDS CRACKIN'! LET'S BEAT FEET TO THE MYSTERY MACHINE!
WHOOOSH

SHAGGY REALLY HADES DAKING A BATH.
BELL, THAD'Z WHY WE CALL HIM "SHAGGY!"

MUNCH! LIKE, WHAT'S THE HOLDUP?
LET'S GO!
OBOY. WE'RE GONNA HAVE DO FUMIGATE THE MYZDERY MACHINE.
MAYBE WE CAN HOLD OUR BREATH THE ENDIRE WAY THERE.

LIKE, THE FASTER WE SOLVE THIS SCENE, THE FASTER SCOOB AND I CAN GET TO OUR CABBAGE-AND-SAUER-KRAUT SANDWICHES!
SO WHERE DO WE START?
RIGHT HERE, YOUNGSTER!
BIG RALPH'S CAR WASH
GAS
ACTIVATE
GASP! DESE PINS ARE NOT WORKING!

I'M BIG RALPH.
THANKS.
FUDGE?

UM... IT'S KINDA, UH, TOUGH.
YEAH, EVERY-BODY SEZ THAT.
KRAK!
KRUNK!
MUH WIFE MADE IT HERSELF.

C'MON, SON, EAT FASTER! OR YUH CAIN'T HAVE MORE-- 'N' THAT'LL MAKE ME MADDER 'N A WET HEN!
NOW, LEMME SHOW YUH TH' BEST DURN CAR WASH THIS SIDE 'A TH' PECOS!
MMMPH! I THINK I, LIKE, CRACKED A MOLAR!
KRIK!

THE DRIVER SPURS HIS MECHANICAL HOSS ONTO TH' CONVEYOR BELT, THEN I PULLS TH' "ACTIVATE" SWITCH T'START TH' WHOLE RIGMAROLE A-WASHIN'.
THAT'S WHEN SHE ALWAYS SHOWS UP.
ACTIVA

SHE? SHE WHO?
MACHINA, THAT'S WHO!
HMMM!
ACTIVATE

SHE'S... A CAR-THING WHAT'S MAD BECAUSE HER AN' HER "SISTER CARS" WAIT ON HUMANITY WITHOUT SO MUCH AS A GRACIAS!

ZHAG, ZCOOBY AND YOU SDAND WADCH HERE WHILE WE LOOK FOR CLUEZ INZIDE. IF YOU ZEE MACHINA, HOLLER.
DON'T WORRY, FRED! LIKE, HOLLERING'S A SPECIALTY OF OURS.

LIKE, WHEW--NOW I CAN DITCH THAT FREAKY FUDGE!
IMAGINE A DESSERT EVEN I COULDN'T EAT!
THIS PLACE'S K-KINDA K-KOOKY, HUH, SCOOB? K-KOOKY IN A SPOOKY K-KINDA WAY!
HM? SNF!

LIKE, WHADAYA SMELL, SCOOBY? IT'S NOT THE, AH, MONSTER, IS IT?
RUH-UH! RESSERT!
ALL RIGHT! I'M STARVING! WE HAVEN'T EATEN FOR, LIKE, A WHOLE FIFTEEN MINUTES!

SNIFFSVILLE, SCOOB! YOU FOUND THE EMPLOYEE BREAK ROOM!
LET'S SEE WHAT KIND OF CHANGE I CAN ARRANGE TO CRACK SOME SNACKS!
SANDWICHES
SNAX
COLD DRINKS

HMMM. WHAT HAVE WE HERE? A TEMPTING ARRAY OF DELECTABLE SANDWICHES.
RANDRICHES. RAPITAL.
SANDWICHES
HAM
CHEEZE
SQUID
ANCHOVY
CRESS
BZZ KLUNK UNK!

AND OVER HERE WE HAVE A LOVELY ARRAY OF CANDY AND SNACKS!
RANDY! MM-MM! RUMPTIOUS!
BZZ KLUNK UNK!

DIG THIS ONE, SCOOB! WHAT'S IT SELL, OIL? IT EVEN LOOKS LIKE A CAR!
RUH... RHAGGY...?

RACHINA!
VRRRM!
NUTT BAR

TENDERFOOTS? WHERE'D YA GET TO?
THOUGHT Y'MIGHT LIKE S'MORE FUDGE!

I'M GONNA CHANGE YOUR OIL!
LIKE, LOOK OUT! COWARD CONVOY COMIN' THROUGH!
WUMP!

DADBURN IT, YOU SPILLED MAH FUDGE!
TRIP
TRIP

I'LL ROTATE YOUR TIRES!
RRELLPP!
AH SHOOT! NOT INTO THE CAR-WASH!

I'LL WASH YOUR WIND-SHIELD!
WE'RE DOOMED!
ACTIVATE
CLIK!

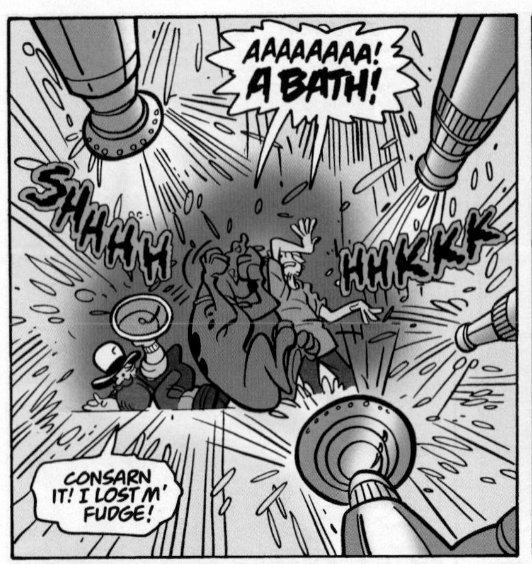
AAAAAAAA! A BATH!
SHHHHH
HHKKK
CONSARN IT! I LOST M' FUDGE!

W-W-WHEW! L-LIKE TH-THAT W-WASN'T S-SO B-BAD!
R-REAH! BRRRR!

SSHHHH
ROAP!
HHHKKKK!
PPFFF! S-SPOKE TOO SOON!

RSHA
RSHA
RSHA
RSHA
AND SCRUBBERS!

IS IT ENDSVILLE YET?
RHI RATE RATHS!

SSHHHK
LIKE THIS IS WORSE THAN MYSTERY SOLVING!
BONK!

SHHHK
ROLD ROLD ROLD!

WHOOOSH
ROT ROT ROT!

MAN, IT'S NOT EASY BEING CLEAN!
RUH-UH!

LOOK OUT, SCOOB! IT'S THE END OF THE LINE!
RUH?
WELL WELL--

--LOOK WHO DROPPED IN FOR A BATH!
ZOINKS!

FRED? DAPHNE? LIKE... LOOK OUT!
BEHIND YOU-- IT'S MA-MACHINA!

VRRRM! I'M GOING TO CHANGE YOUR OIL!
VELMA!?

SORRY WE HAD TO FOOL YOU GUYS, BUT THERE WAS NO OTHER WAY YOU WOULD TAKE A BATH!
Y-YOU MEAN...? THIS WHOLE MYSTERY A PUT-ON? THERE IS NO MONSTER...?
THAT'S RIGHT! NO MONSTER--
BLBL...

--EXCEPT THAT ONE!
JINKIES!
BLBB-B!

IT'S RIGHT BEHIND US!
AROUND THIS CORNER, GANG! QUICKLY!
EXIT

RALPH'S CAR WASH
LIKE, THERE'S SOMETHING AWFULLY *FAMILIAR* ABOUT THIS HIDING SPOT, FRED!
BLBL BL!
ACTIVATE

CAR
OH, NO! LIKE, HERE WE GO AGAIN!
HASTA LA VISTA, TENDERFOOTS!
SHOONK!

I DIDN'T MIND HELPIN' THEM GREEN-HORNS WITH THEIR BATH--
--HECK, I NEEDED ONE MUHSELF, TONIGHT BEING SATURDAY AN' ALL!
MY HAIR!
MY GLASSES!
BUT AFTER THEY WRECKED MUH WIFE'S FUDGE, WELL...

LIKE I SAID, IT MADE ME MADDER 'N A *REALLY* WET HEN!
TWO BATHS IN ONE DAY? I'LL **MELT**!
REEELP!
JANE! STOP THIS CRAZY THING!
THE END

LAST OF THE MUGWUMPS
LIKE--WHEN DO WE STOP FOR BREAKFAST? I'M STARVED.
RE ROO!
WE'VE ONLY BEEN ON THE ROAD FOR HALF AN HOUR!
JOE EDKIN STORY JOE STATON PENCILS DAVE HUNT INKS
JOHN COSTANZA LETTERS PAUL BECTON COLORS HARVEY RICHARDS ASSISTS
HEIDI MacDONALD, EDITS
GRRRRRR
THERE'S A TOWN TEN MILES AHEAD. WE CAN STOP TO EAT THERE, SHAGGY.
GOOD THING, FRED. MY STOMACH'S GROWLING LIKE A BEAR!
GRRR RRR
EAST MOSSVILLE
GUYS, I DON'T THINK SHAGGY'S STOMACH IS MAKING THAT NOISE.
LOOKS LIKE THE MYSTERY MACHINE NEEDS MORE THAN A TUNEUP!
THE MYSTERY MACHINE
YIKES! WE'D BETTER STOP AT A GARAGE WHEN WE GET TO TOWN!
GRRRRR

LOOKS LIKE YA GOT HERE JUST IN TIME, YOUNG MAN. GONE MUCH FURTHER, AN' IT MIGHTA LEFT YOU STRANDED IN THE 'GLADES.
HOW LONG WILL IT TAKE YOU TO FIX IT, SIR?
MECHANIC ON DUTY
GONNA HAVE T'ORDER PARTS. MAY BE A COUPLE DAYS.
JINKIES! WHERE ARE WE GOING TO STAY UNTIL IT'S READY?
THERE'S A MOTEL UP THE ROAD A WAYS, MISS VELMA. I CAN GIVE YA A RIDE IN MY TRUCK.
LIKE, I HOPE THEY HAVE A RESTAURANT. THESE CANDY BARS ARE HARDLY ENOUGH TO TIDE US OVER-- RIGHT, SCOOB?
BUD'S
RIGHT!
WHAT'S GOING ON HERE, MR. PARSONS?
LOOKS LIKE SOME KIND OF PROTEST, MISS DAPHNE DUNNO WHAT THE RUCKUS IS ABOUT.
EAST MOSSVILLE MOTOR LODGE
SAVE OUR SWAMP
BUD'S AUTO SERVICE
HEY, GUYS! I'M MARK McMURRAY AND THIS IS GRIFF. YOU HERE TO JOIN OUR PROTEST?
WHAT ARE YOU PROTESTING?
THERE'S A GROUP OF LAND DEVELOPERS HERE TO BUY UP SOME OF THE EVERGLADES.
IF THEY BUILD IN THE 'GLADES, IT COULD RUIN THE DELICATE ECOSYSTEM AND DRIVE AWAY THE LAST OF THE MUGWUMPS.
MUGWUMPS?
THEY WERE MONSTROUS BEASTS THAT WERE SAID TO GUARD THE TREASURES OF THE EVERGLADES. WORD IS, THERE'S ONLY ONE LEFT. WE HAVE TO SAVE IT!
MUGWUMPS? MUGWUMPS? WHERE HAVE I HEARD THAT BEFORE?
ZOINKS! LAND DEVELOPERS! MONSTERS! TREASURE! LIKE, YOU KNOW THIS CAN'T BE GOOD!

ROOOOAARRRRR!
IS THAT THE MUGWUMP?
I'M NOT GOING TO STICK AROUND TO ASK!
RE REITHER!
SAVE OUR SWAMP
WHAT DO YOU SUPPOSE THAT THING IS?
FROM THE LOOKS OF IT-- I'D SAY "MAD!"
I COULD RUN FASTER IF WE'D HAD BREAKFAST!
GANGWAY!
LET'S LEAF THIS MONSTER BEHIND!

RO RAWAY!
WHY DON'T YOU GO BARK UP THE WRONG TREE?
THAT'S NOT WHAT I MEANT!
VELMA! GRIFF! LOOK OUT BEHIND YOU!
OOF!
LEAVE HER ALONE!
WHERE ARE MY GLASSES?
WHAP!

REGIST
GET OUT OF FLORIDA! WE DON'T WANT YOU HERE!
WHO'S THAT?
TAMARA PELLEK. SHE'S THE PERSON WHO BROUGHT THE DEVELOPERS TO EAST MOSSVILLE.
BAIT
MAPS
NEWS
RENT-A-BU
MY ASSOCIATES AND I ARE ONLY HERE TO STUDY THE LAND. WE HAVE NOT MADE A DECISION ON HOW IT WILL BE USED YET.
IF YOU DON'T INTEND TO DO ANY HARM, MS. PELLEK, WHY ARE YOU HANDING OUT RIFLES?
IF WHAT THESE PROTESTORS SAY IS TRUE ABOUT THE MUGWUMP, WE MAY HAVE TO PROTECT OURSELVES.
BUT YOU CAN'T KILL THE LAST OF THE SPECIES!
THESE FIRE TRANQUILIZER DARTS.
IT WILL ONLY PUT THE CREATURE TO SLEEP!
LIKE--WE'VE BEEN OUT HERE FOR AN HOUR AND WE HAVEN'T SEEN A THING EXCEPT SPANISH MOSS.
AND WE STILL HAVEN'T EATEN!
REAH!
ROOAARRR!
ROOAARR!
YIKES! I SPOKE TOO SOON!

WHAT'S ON THE MUGWUMP'S FOOT?
IT FEELS LIKE--
HOPE YOU DON'T MIND US DROPPING IN!
ROTTA RELP RELMA!

WHO?
IT'S ME--SHAGGY--YOUR KNIGHT IN KHAKI ARMOR!

RIKES!
WE'VE GOTTA STOP THAT THING!

YOW--WE'VE GOT TO GET YOU A DROOL BIB, SCOOB!

THE TRANQUILIZER IN THOSE DARTS MIGHT BE TOXIC TO THE MUGWUMP!
STOP!
IF MR. MCMURRAY AND HIS FRIENDS ARE RIGHT, WE CAN'T AFFORD TO TAKE ANY CHANCES THAT MIGHT HARM THE MUGWUMP.
LIKE-- SINCE WHEN DO WE PROTECT MONSTERS?
IT'S NOT A MONSTER! I FINALLY REMEMBERED WHAT A MUGWUMP IS!
WHAT??
THEY WERE HUMANS--"RADICAL" REPUBLICANS WHO REFUSED TO SUPPORT THEIR PARTY'S PRESIDENTIAL CANDIDATE JAMES G. BLAINE IN THE 1884 ELECTION AGAINST GROVER CLEVELAND.
WHAT'S MORE, WHEN I WAS AT THE MONSTER'S FEET-- I'M SURE I SAW A ZIPPER.
BUT WHO COULD THE MUGWUMP BE? LIKE--WE'VE GOT TOO MANY LAND DEVELOPERS TO CHOOSE FROM!
WHEN WAS THE LAST TIME WE SAW MS. PELLEK?
IT'S TIME TO SET A TRAP! WE'LL NEED A CHAINSAW AND SOME ROPE!
RUH-ROH!

LIKE, WHY ARE WE ALWAYS THE BAIT?
RI RON'T ROW.
C'MON, GUYS! WE GAVE YOU SOME SCOOBY SNACKS!
AND JUST IN TIME! I WAS ABOUT TO PASS OUT FROM HUNGER.
REAH-- RUNGER!
ZZZZZ
ZZZZZZ
WHAT DO YOU THINK YOU'RE DOING? I PROMISED WE WOULDN'T CAUSE ANY DAMAGE!
MS. PELLEK! WHAT ARE YOU DOING HERE? I MEAN--DRESSED LIKE THAT!
WE THOUGHT YOU WERE THE MUGWUMP!
ZZZZZZ
WHY WOULD YOU THINK THAT?
YOU'RE A LAND DEVELOPER AND YOU WEREN'T AROUND WHEN IT SHOWED UP!
I WAS TAKING PICTURES.
ZZZZ

ROOAARRRRR!
THERE'S YOUR REAL BEASTIE!
ZZZZZZ
SPLOOSH

RON'T ROOT!
WE HAVE A TRAP SET UP!

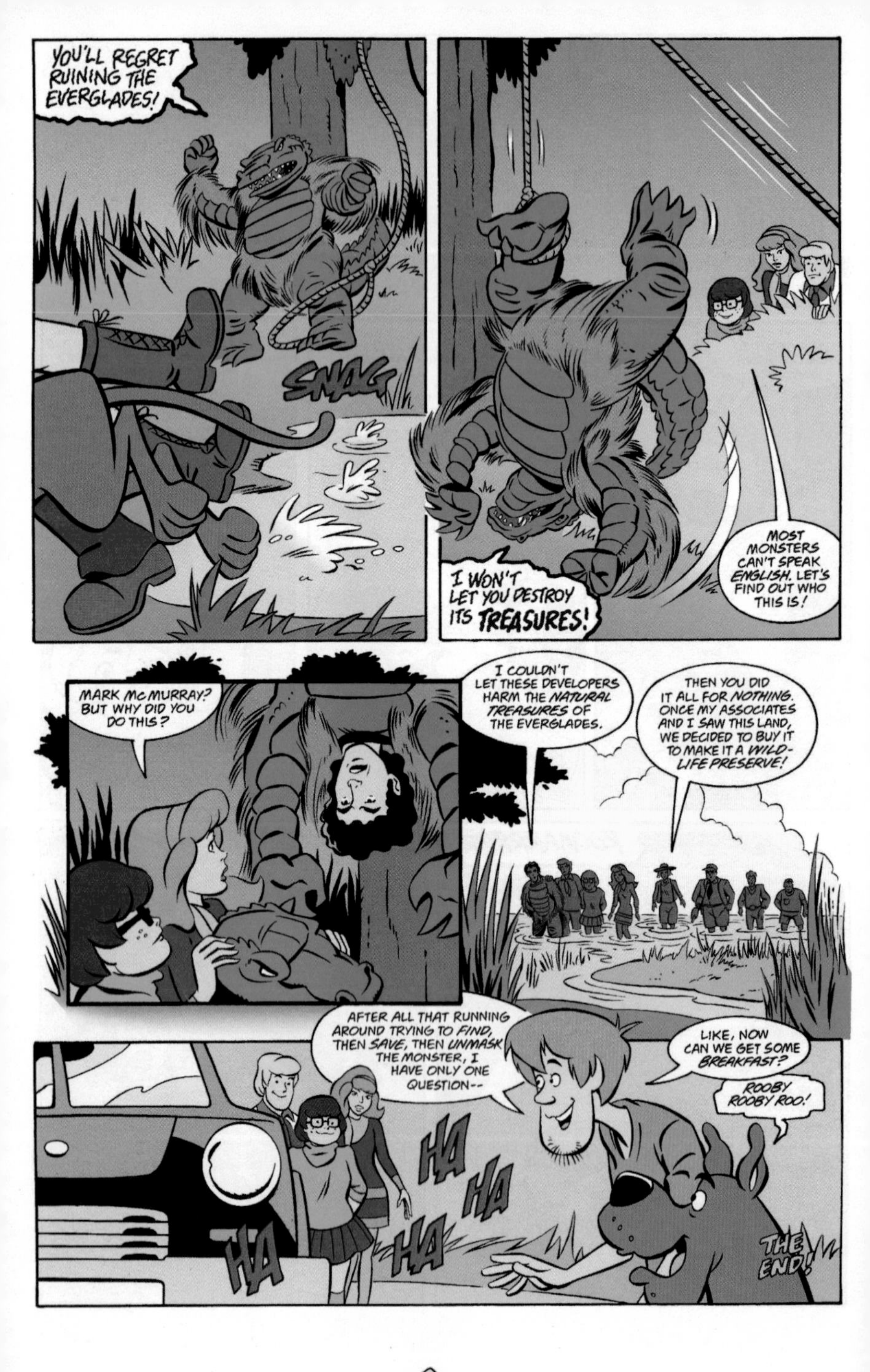
YOU'LL REGRET RUINING THE EVERGLADES!
SNAG
I WON'T LET YOU DESTROY ITS TREASURES!
MOST MONSTERS CAN'T SPEAK ENGLISH. LET'S FIND OUT WHO THIS IS!
MARK McMURRAY? BUT WHY DID YOU DO THIS?
I COULDN'T LET THESE DEVELOPERS HARM THE NATURAL TREASURES OF THE EVERGLADES.
THEN YOU DID IT ALL FOR NOTHING. ONCE MY ASSOCIATES AND I SAW THIS LAND, WE DECIDED TO BUY IT TO MAKE IT A WILD-LIFE PRESERVE!
AFTER ALL THAT RUNNING AROUND TRYING TO FIND, THEN SAVE, THEN UNMASK THE MONSTER, I HAVE ONLY ONE QUESTION--
LIKE, NOW CAN WE GET SOME BREAKFAST?
ROOBY ROOBY ROO!
HA HA HA HA HA
THE END!

THE LIBRARY LURKER
writer JOHN ROZUM
penciller ANTHONY WILLIAMS
inker JIM AMASH
letterer COSTANZA
colorist PAUL BECTON
assistant editor HARVEY RICHARDS
editor HEIDI MacDONALD

HEY! HOW COME YOU GET ALL THE LEFTOVER FOOD?
ROGGY RAGS!
BREAKFAST SPECIAL

I SURE WISH WE HAD TIME TO STICK AROUND AND SOLVE THIS MYSTERY!
FORGET IT, FRED. WE'RE ALREADY RUNNING LATE!
COOLSVILLE COURIER
BEASLEY JEWELS STOLEN
THIEVES STEAL BOOK SAFE FULL OF GEMS

HEY, WHAT'S THIS?
UH-OH, NOW VELMA'S AT IT!

"TREASURE ISLAND." IT'S A LIBRARY BOOK AND IT'S WAY OVERDUE!
TREASURE ISLAND
TREASURE ISLAND ROBERT LOUIS STEVENSON
THE LIBRARY'S RIGHT NEXT TO WHERE WE PARKED THE MYSTERY MACHINE. LET'S DROP IT OFF.

LIKE, AS LONG AS WE DON'T HAVE TO READ IT. THAT PIRATE, LONG JOHN SILVER, GIVES ME THE CREEPS.
BRRR

JEEPERS! THIS PLACE IS ENORMOUS.
AND DARK. LIKE, HOW CAN ANYBODY READ IN THIS DIM LIGHT?
WHERE IS EVERYBODY?

HELLO?
HELLO HELLO HELLO
REEPY.
LIKE, YOU SAID IT, SCOOB. LET'S RETURN THAT BOOK AND GET OUT OF HERE.

OKAY, THERE'S THE RETURN COUNTER.
I WONDER WHY NOBODY'S MANNING THE DESK?
BECAUSE I ORDERED THEM TO LEAVE!

LONG JOHN SILVER!
LIKE, I THOUGHT HE WAS ONLY MAKE-BELIEVE.
SO DID I!
LEAVE, LEST YOU WANTS TO BE SWINGING FROM A JIB-ARM INSTEAD.

LIKE, I HAVE NO IDEA WHAT HE JUST SAID, BUT I AGREE WITH HIM COMPLETELY!
RHEE TOO!
SHAGGY, SCOOBY, WAIT!
YOU'RE GOING THE WRONG WAY!
SO WHICH WAY IS THE RIGHT WAY, FRED?
I THOUGHT IT WAS THIS WAY.
JINKIES, WE'RE LOST TOO!

YOU CERTAINLY ARE, LASSIE. IN MORE WAYS THAN YOU THINK.
LET'S SPLIT UP! HE CAN'T FOLLOW US ALL!

AYE. YOU COULD AT THAT. ONLY I HAVE MY OWN CREW OF TREACHEROUS VILLAINS FROM LITERATURE.

INJUN JOE FROM THE ADVENTURES OF TOM SAWYER.
I RECKON THAT'D BE FRANKENSTEIN'S MONSTER RETURNING WITH YOUR WAYWARD SCALAWAGS.
RELP!
TREACHEROUS VILLAINS, EH? THEN WHO'S THE LITTLE GUY?
ME? I'M DR. JEKYLL.
GULP GULP
AND I'M MR. HYDE.
ANYTHING ELSE YOU'D LIKE TO KNOW?
YEAH, LIKE SPEAKING OF HYDE...
YOU KNOW ANY PLACES WE CAN HIDE?
RUN FOR IT!

WHEW! THAT WAS CLOSE. VELMA, WHAT DID YOU COME UP WITH?

I SCANNED THE BARCODE IN THE BACK OF THAT COPY OF TREASURE ISLAND AND FOUND OUT THAT IT WAS CHECKED OUT TO SOMEONE CALLED TIM LEHNERT.
HE ALSO CHECKED OUT THE BOOKS THAT THE OTHER VILLAINS CAME FROM.
THEN HE'S OUR MAN! GOOD WORK, VELMA.

HERE'S ANOTHER CLUE! THIS BOOK-MARK IS REALLY A RECEIPT FROM A COSTUME SUPPLY STORE.
PIRATE COSTUMES, INDIAN WIGS, GREEN MAKEUP, BLACK LIGHTS, A FOG MACHINE AND SOME OTHER STUFF.
I'VE GOT AN IDEA!
FIRST WE'VE GOT TO FIND WHERE THEY'RE HIDING THE REST OF THEIR SUPPLIES!
TREASURE ISLAND

ZOINKS! I'M TOO SCARED TO LOOK. ARE THEY GONE, SCOOB?
ROOK, RAGGY!
A FOG MACHINE! I WONDER WHAT A LIBRARY NEEDS WITH ONE OF THOSE?
YOU'D BETTER TURN IT OFF, SCOOB, BEFORE THOSE VILLAINS SPOT THE SMOKE.
FOG
MACHINE
CLICK
LOW SPEED
FULL SPEED
ROOPS.
TURN IT OFF! TURN IT OFF, SCOOB!
RAN'T REE RACHINE!
WHAT DO YOU MEAN YOU CAN'T SEE THE MACHINE-- WAIT, WHAT'S THAT NOISE?
CLUMP
CLUMP
CLUMP
CLUMP
CLUMP
I THINK THEY FOUND US, SCOOB!
MAYBE THEY'LL LOSE US IN THIS FOG BANK!
AYE, WE HAVE.
NOT SO FAST, LADDIE. I BE HOLDING THE REMOTE CONTROL WHICH'LL TURN OFF THAT ALL-ENGULFING FOG.
CLICK!

THAT'S *ALL* WE NEEDED TO HEAR.
THERE ARE YOUR JEWEL THIEVES, MRS. BEASLEY.

THEY USED A COMBINATION OF COSTUMES AND SPECIAL EFFECTS TO SCARE PEOPLE AWAY FROM THE LIBRARY.
DR. JEKYLL CHANGED INTO MR. HYDE USING SPECIAL MAKEUP THAT ONLY SHOWED UP UNDER A BLACK LIGHT, JUST LIKE THE WITCH'S EVIL SPIRITS.

WE WERE ABLE TO SOLVE THE CASE BECAUSE LONG JOHN-- I MEAN TIM LEHNERT-- LEFT THE RECEIPT FROM THE COSTUME STORE IN THE COPY OF TREASURE ISLAND HE CHECKED OUT.
BUT WHO'S THE WITCH? SHE'S NOT ONE OF US.

TA-DA, IT'S JUST *ME*, DAPHNE.

THERE'S JUST ONE UNSOLVED PART TO THIS MYSTERY. WHERE ARE THE JEWELS?
I THINK I CAN SOLVE THAT, YOUNG MAN.

BEEP-BEEP
BEEP-BEEP

I'VE SOMETIMES FORGOTTEN WHERE I'VE SHELVED THIS BOOK ON MY OWN LIBRARY AT HOME, SO I HAD THIS LOCATOR INSTALLED IN THE BINDING.
WELL, I GUESS THAT WRAPS UP THIS CASE.

YOU'RE OVERLOOKING ONE LITTLE PIECE OF UNSOLVED BUSINESS-- WHERE DID SHAGGY AND SCOOBY VANISH TO?
I THINK I KNOW THE ANSWER TO THAT!

...ROIL RAND RERVE!
SOUNDS MOUTHWATERING, SCOOB! HOW ABOUT THIS ONE-- POTATOES AU GRATIN WITH SAUTEED SPIN--
SHAGGY! SCOOBY!
Recipes
COOKERY
COOK BOOK

THERE YOU ARE! IT'S TIME TO GO. WE'RE ALREADY BEHIND SCHEDULE.
RHUT, RE'RE REST RETTING TO RUH ROOD RART!
NOW, SCOOBY. YOU TOO, SHAGGY.
OKAY, OKAY, WE GET THE PICTURE, DAPHNE.
SOMETIMES YOU CAN BE SUCH A WITCH.
The End

VENICE, THE CITY OF ROMANCE.
AND WHAT COULD BE MORE ROMANTIC THAN DREAMING AWAY AN EVENING IN A GONDOLA ON ITS CANALS?
OH, CHUCK! THE STARS ARE BEAUTIFUL TONIGHT!
NOT AS BEAUTIFUL AS YOU, MY DARLING!
DID WE SAY DREAMING?
MAKE THAT...HAVING A NIGHTMARE!
BWA-HA-HA-HA-HA!
THE ITALIAN HELLION!
EEEEEEEK!
HELP! IT'S THE PHANTOM OF THE CANALS!
WRITER: DAN ABNETT
PENCILS: ANTHONY WILLIAMS
INKS: JEFF ALBRECHT
LETTERER: JENNA GARCIA
COLORIST: PAUL BECTON
SEPARATOR: DIGITAL CHAMELEON
ASST. EDITOR: HARVEY RICHARDS
EDITOR: JOAN HILTY

MEANWHILE...
LIKE, I CAN'T WAIT TO HIT OLD VENICE, SCOOB!
SPAGHETTI! MEATBALLS! AND, LIKE, TAKE A LOOK AT ALL THAT ICE CREAM!
RUM RUM, RAGGY!
...AND OF COURSE, IT'S SUCH A HISTORIC CITY WITH AMAZING BUILDINGS AND CANALS AND ALL!
VENICE
IT'S ALL SO ROMANTIC...
LIKE, I AGREE!
YOU, ROMANTIC?
YEAH, WHY NOT? I HAVE FEELINGS TOO, Y'KNOW!
VENIC
OH SCOOBY!
ROH RHAGGY!
HA! THEY'VE JUST FALLEN IN LOVE WITH THE ANNUAL GELATO FESTIVAL... RIGHT, GUYS?
FESTIVAL GELATO
BUT SHORTLY...
VENICE SURE SEEMS QUIETER THAN I EXPECTED.
LIKE, MAYBE THEY'RE ALL RESTING UP BEFORE THE BIG GELATO FESTIVAL?

IT'S DESERTED!
YEAH, BUT, LIKE, TOMORROW IT'LL BE DESSERTED, RIGHT?
SOMETHING STRANGE IS GOING ON.
NOT STRANGE! DELICIOUS! GELATO FEST? REMEMBER?
COME ON, GUYS! LIKE, WORK WITH ME!
THERE'S NO MYSTERY HERE! NO GHOULS! NO WEIRD HAPPENINGS!
CAN'T WE HAVE, LIKE, JUST ONE FOREIGN TRIP WHERE THERE IS NO MYSTERY?
JUST GELATO! NICE, SAFE, UN-MYSTERIOUS YUMMY GELATO! WHAT DO YOU SAY? HUH?
DID YOU JUST SEE THAT?
SEE WHAT?
IT MUST HAVE BEEN A TRICK OF THE LIGHT!
GUYS, LIKE, SEE WHAT?
IT LOOKED FOR ALL THE WORLD LIKE A....PHANTOM GONDOLIER!
SCOOB! THEY'RE DOING IT AGAIN! THEY'RE GETTING MYSTERIOUS! THEY'RE SPOILING THE GELATO!
RI ROW, RAGGY, RI ROW!

LADIES, GENTLEMEN... CAN I TAKE YOU TO YOUR HOTEL, PERHAPS?
WHY DON'T YOU AND DAPHNE GO AHEAD WITH THE LUGGAGE, FRED? WE'LL FOLLOW ON FOOT.
OH, LET'S, FREDDY! IT'LL BE SO ROMA--
--I MEAN, FUN.
MY, THIS IS LOVELY, ISN'T IT, FREDDY?
SURE IS, DAPH!
SAY, FRIEND! HAVE YOU HEARD ANYTHING ABOUT A PHANTOM GONDOLIER?
JUST A MYTH, SIGNORE--AN OLD STORY!
THERE CAN BE A LOT TO THOSE OLD TALES, SIR.
HMPH! MORE INTERESTED IN THE GHOST, AS USUAL!
BWA-HA-HA-HA-HA!
MAMA MIA! NOT AGAIN!
WOW!
YIKES!

SO...UM... HOW WAS YOUR ROMANTIC RIDE DOWN THE CANAL?
OUR GONDOLA WAS CAPSIZED BY THE PHANTOM OF THE CANALS.
WE HAD TO SWIM THE REST OF THE WAY.
JINKIES, DAPHNE! THAT'S AWFUL!
DID YOU GET A GOOD LOOK AT THIS PHANTOM?
NO--IT ALL HAPPENED SO QUICKLY!
GUYS...YOU'VE BEEN THROUGH A LOT. YOU'VE, LIKE, FOUND A MYSTERY WHERE THERE DIDN'T NEED TO BE ONE.
I HAVE THE PERFECT PICK-YOU-UP...
...A MEGA-SIZE SERVING OF GELATO!
UH-OH. THIS IS GOING TO HAVE TO BE ON SOMEONE ELSE.
I THINK I LOST MY WALLET WHEN THAT PHANTOM SCARED US OVERBOARD!
OH, NO! NOT THE PHANTOM AGAIN!

YOU KNOW ABOUT THAT, SIGNORE?
VENICE IS THE CITY OF LOVE, BUT THE LOVERS, THEY ARE STAYING AWAY!
SOON I WILL GO OUT OF BUSINESS... THEN NO MORE GELATO!

IT IS ALL THE FAULT OF THE PHANTOM...
...A GONDOLIER COME BACK TO HAUNT THE CITY. HE HAS FRIGHTENED AWAY ALL THE LOVERS. IT IS TERRIBLE!
DON'T YOU WORRY, SIGNORE-- WE'LL PUT THIS PHANTOM GONDOLIER OUT OF BUSINESS! WON'T WE, GANG?

RIGHT RON, RELMA!
THANKS, SCOOB.
RACTUALLY, RAT RAS RAGGY...

THE NEXT EVENING...
WE DIDN'T FIND MUCH--EXCEPT THIS SASH ON ONE OF THE BRIDGES.

CAFE
IT IS VERY OLD! MAYBE IT BELONGS TO THE PHANTOM!
CAN YOU GUYS TAKE US BACK TO WHERE YOU FOUND IT?

HEY SHAGGY! SCOOBY! NO TIME FOR FOOD NOW! THERE'S A MYSTERY WAITING!
BUT IT'S LIKE, DINNERTIME! IF IT WAS REALLY TIME FOR A MYSTERY, THEY'D CALL IT, LIKE, "MYSTERY-TIME"!
MENU
WE'LL GET SOMETHING TO EAT LATER!

DON'T YOU WORRY. HERE'S SOMETHING TO KEEP YOU GOING UNTIL SUPPER!
LIKE, THANKS!
FOLLOW US AND WE'LL SHOW YOU WHERE WE FOUND THE SASH.
LIKE, I'LL DRIVE, SCOOBY, WHILE YOU FIX US A LITTLE SNACK!
A FEW MINUTES LATER...
THAT'S IT! THAT'S WHERE WE FOUND THE SASH!
IT ALL LOOKS PRETTY QUIET. LET'S SPLIT UP AND SEARCH THE AREA!
LIKE, WE'LL JUST STAND WATCH UNDER THE BRIDGE. OKAY, SCOOB?
ROKAY, RHAGGY.
TEEHEE! GREAT RIDEA, RHAGGY!
LIKE, THANKS, SCOOB!

BWA-HA-HA-HA!
UH OH! SCOOB! THERE REALLY IS A PHANTOM!
RIKES!
SCOOBY! LET'S, LIKE, GET OUT OF HERE!
RI'M RYING... ROWCH!
SKWELCHH
COUGH! SPLUTTER!
THE GELATO!
NOOOOOOOO!

NOOOO!
WHAT WAS THAT?
SHAGGY! HE AND SCOOBY MUST BE IN TERRIBLE TROUBLE!
WE HAVE TO HELP THEM!
JINKIES! THAT SOUNDED LIKE SHAGGY IN MORTAL TERROR!
DON'T WORRY, GUYS! I'M ON MY WAY!
A GONDOLIER WITHOUT A GONDOLA...
...HMMM! THAT'S MIGHTY SUSPICIOUS!
AND HE APPEARS TO HAVE LOST HIS SASH...
...OUR MYSTERY PHANTOM, I WONDER?
HEY, MISTER PHANTOM...
...HERE'S A LITTLE TRIP FOR SPOILING OURS!
K-SPLASH

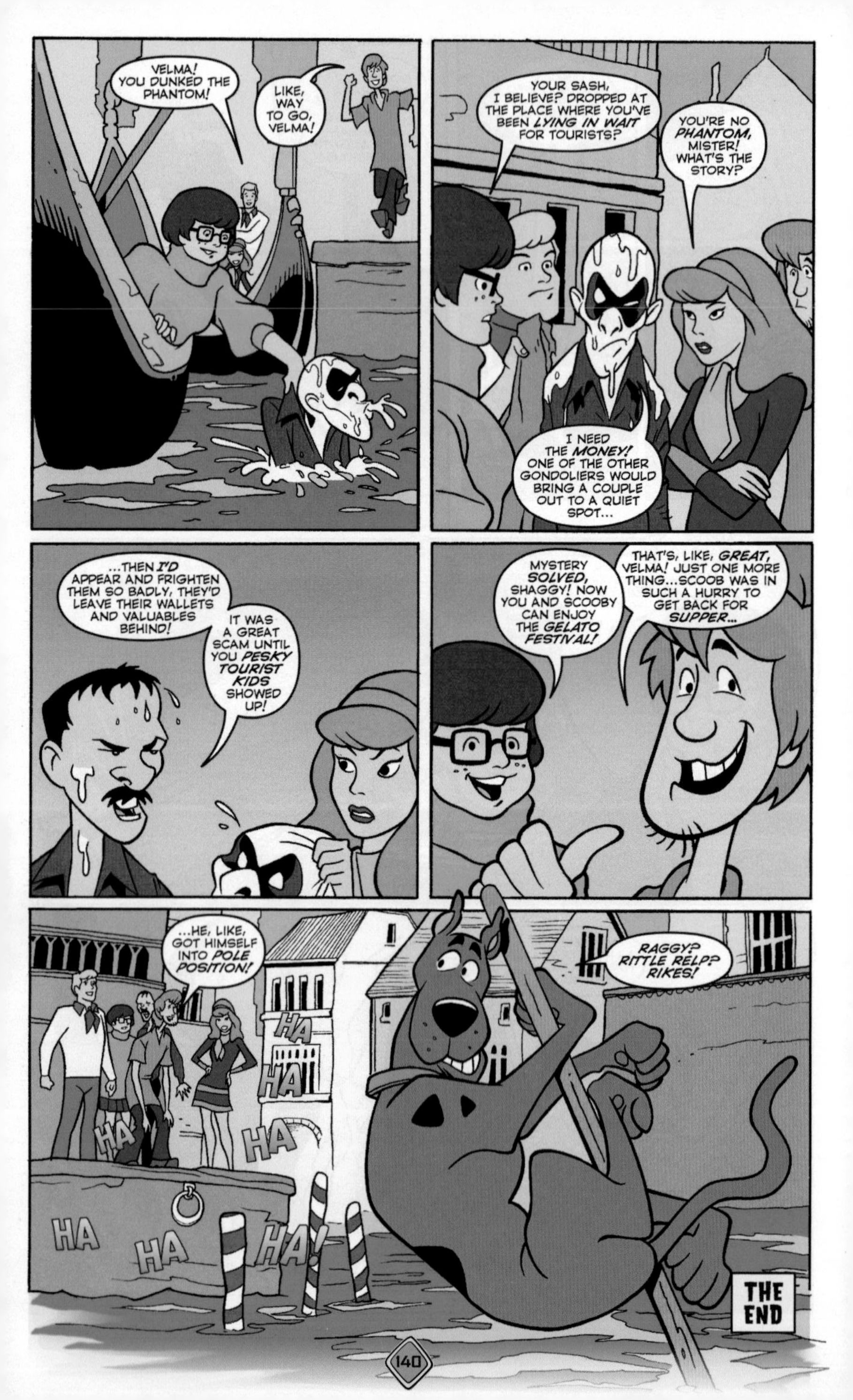
VELMA! YOU DUNKED THE PHANTOM!
LIKE, WAY TO GO, VELMA!
YOUR SASH, I BELIEVE? DROPPED AT THE PLACE WHERE YOU'VE BEEN LYING IN WAIT FOR TOURISTS?
YOU'RE NO PHANTOM, MISTER! WHAT'S THE STORY?
I NEED THE MONEY! ONE OF THE OTHER GONDOLIERS WOULD BRING A COUPLE OUT TO A QUIET SPOT...
...THEN I'D APPEAR AND FRIGHTEN THEM SO BADLY, THEY'D LEAVE THEIR WALLETS AND VALUABLES BEHIND!
IT WAS A GREAT SCAM UNTIL YOU PESKY TOURIST KIDS SHOWED UP!
MYSTERY SOLVED, SHAGGY! NOW YOU AND SCOOBY CAN ENJOY THE GELATO FESTIVAL!
THAT'S, LIKE, GREAT, VELMA! JUST ONE MORE THING...SCOOB WAS IN SUCH A HURRY TO GET BACK FOR SUPPER...
...HE, LIKE, GOT HIMSELF INTO POLE POSITION!
RAGGY? RITTLE RELP? RIKES!
HA HA HA HA HA HA HA!
THE END

The MYSTERY MACHINE MYSTERY
ROZUM writer • STATON penciller • PEPOY inker
COSTANZA letterer • BECTON colorist • RICHARDS assists
MacDONALD & HILTY edits
SEPTEMBER.
THE MYSTERY MACHINE
POOM!
LIKE, WHY'D IT HAVE TO BE RIGHT OUTSIDE THAT CREEPY OLD MANSION?
UH-OH, I THINK WE JUST BLEW A TIRE.
WE'LL NEVER CRACK THE TESTAROSSA CASE NOW!
NOVEMBER.
WELL, GANG, IT LOOKS LIKE WE'VE GOT A FLAT TIRE.
AT LEAST IT DIDN'T HAPPEN BEFORE WE PUT AWAY THE FERRARI GANG.
LIKE, WHY'D IT HAVE TO BE RIGHT NEAR THAT SPOOKY OLD STEAMBOAT?
MARCH.
WELL, GANG, THE SPARE'S NO GOOD EITHER. LET'S SPLIT UP AND SEE IF WE CAN FIND THE GROUNDSKEEPER.
=GULP!= LIKE, WHY DON'T WE EVER BREAK DOWN IN FRONT OF A LUXURY HOTEL?
APRIL
WELL, GANG, THERE'S NOTHING I CAN DO TO FIX IT. MAYBE THERE'S A PHONE IN THAT OLD HOTEL!
ZOINKS! WHY COULDN'T IT HAVE BEEN A DIFFERENT LUXURY HOTEL?
LUXURY HOTEL
VACANCY

TODAY.
HOW DOES IT LOOK, FREDDIE?
GOLD NUGGET LUXURY HOTEL and SALOO
NOT GOOD.

SHE'S BEEN WITH US A LONG TIME, BUT I THINK SHE'S DRIVEN HER LAST MILE.
I HATE TO SAY IT, BUT...

IT'S TIME TO BUY A NEW MYSTERY MACHINE.

LIKE, WHERE ARE WE GOING TO FIND A CAR DEALERSHIP OUT HERE IN THE MIDDLE OF THIS SPOOKY OLD GHOST TOWN?

WE'RE NOT, SHAGGY. WE'RE GOING BACK INTO TOWN ON ONE OF THOSE TOUR BUSES. WE'LL FIND A DEALERSHIP ONCE WE'RE THERE.
LIVERY
TOURZ
Apothec

CONGRATULATIONS, FREDDIE. YOU CAN PICK IT UP ANYTIME TOMORROW AFTER NINE O'CLOCK IN THE MORNING.
THANKS! I'LL SEE YOU THEN.
YOU BOUGHT A NEW VAN?
WHERE IS IT? WHEN DO WE GET TO SEE IT?
NOT UNTIL TOMORROW. THEY'RE GIVING IT A CUSTOM PAINT JOB.
YOU REMEMBERED TO GET SOMETHING WITH BUILT-IN DRINK CUP HOLDERS, DIDN'T YOU, FREDDIE?
AND A SNACK BAR, RIGHT?
YES.
YES, SHAGGY.
HEH-HEH-HEH

THE NEXT MORNING...
GEE, I'M SO EXCITED. I'LL MISS THE OLD MYSTERY MACHINE, BUT IT IS ABOUT TIME WE GOT A NEW ONE.
OTUA
SO, GANG, WHAT DO YOU THINK?
THE MYSTERY MACHINE
JINKIES!
LIKE, FAR OUT!
GROOVY!
RAWESOME!
SO WHAT DO YOU SAY WE TAKE HER FOR A SPIN?

THE MYSTERY MACHINE
VROOOOOOOM!!
LIKE, CHECK OUT ALL THESE CRAZY GADGETS! THIS AM/FM STEREO WITH A CD PLAYER IS A REAL STEP UP FROM THAT 8-TRACK IN THE OLD MYSTERY MACHINE.
YEAH, AND IT HANDLES LIKE A DREAM!
FREDDIE! LOOK OUT!
SWERVE
SCREEECH
YOU WERE SAYING, FREDDIE?
ER, LOOKS LIKE IT'S HANDLING MORE LIKE A NIGHTMARE RIGHT NOW!
I DON'T KNOW WHAT HAPPENED. IT'S FIGHTING ME, AS IF IT WERE TRYING TO CRASH US ON PURPOSE.
AND IT'S DOING A GOOD JOB TOO! ZOINKS! WATCH OUT!
SCREEECH!!
CAUTION
THE MYSTERY MACHINE
THUMP

IT'S ALMOST AS IF THE MYSTERY MACHINE WAS HAUNTED.
HAUNTED?!
MWAH-HAH-HAH-HAH-HAH!

HOW RIGHT YOU ARE. AND THIS IS ONE GHOST YOU CAN'T UN-MASK.
ESPECIALLY WHEN YOU'RE SOON TO BECOME GHOSTS YOURSELVES.
ZOINKS!

FRED, LOOK, THERE'S A BLACK VAN FOLLOWING US.
I SEE IT, DAPHNE.

AND LIKE THERE'S A REALLY HIGH BRIDGE UP AHEAD!
R'OH-NO!

"DEAD DROP GORGE." ZOINKS, I DON'T LIKE THE SOUND OF THAT.
DEAD DROP GORGE BRIDGE
IF I DON'T REGAIN CONTROL OF THE WHEEL, THERE'S GOING TO BE A SOUND YOU LIKE EVEN LESS.
LIKE, WHAT COULD THAT BE?
US HITTING THE BOTTOM OF DEAD DROP GORGE.

GULP!

HMMM.
A BUG.
LIKE, WHAT'S THAT?
RUG? :YECCH:
NOT THAT KIND OF BUG, SCOOBY. IT'S AN ELECTRONIC LISTENING DEVICE. IT'S ALSO A CLUE.
FRED, DAPHNE, HERE'S WHAT I NEED YOU BOTH TO DO...
HERE GOES. I HOPE EVERYONE'S BUCKLED UP.
LIKE, I SURE HOPE YOU HAVE INSURANCE.
NOW, DAPHNE!
SCREECH!!!
CRASH!!
THE MYSTERY MACHINE

IS EVERYONE SURE THEY'RE OKAY?
YEAH, BUT NO THANKS TO THIS GUY!
TOW
WHO IS HE?
HIS NAME'S PHILIP SCREW-DRIVER. HE WAS THE MECHANIC OF A VILLAINOUS RACE CAR DRIVER NAMED STANLEY TESTARROSSA WHO WE HELPED PUT BEHIND BARS SOME TIME AGO.
THEN HE WORKED WITH THE FERRARI GANG, A BUNCH OF ROBBERS WHO USED HIGH-SPEED GETAWAY VEHICLES. WE PUT THEM BEHIND BARS, TOO.
HE MUST HAVE BEEN PLANNING REVENGE. WHEN WE BOUGHT THE NEW MYSTERY MACHINE HE GOT HIS CHANCE BY RIGGING THE STEERING TO A REMOTE CONTROL HE WAS OPERATING.
AND I ALMOST GOT AWAY WITH IT, TOO. YOU KIDS MEDDLE TOO MUCH.
WELL, HE CERTAINLY MADE SURE YOU WON'T EVER BE DRIVING YOUR NEW RIG AGAIN.
THAT'S OKAY, OFFICER...
"I HAVE ANOTHER VEHICLE THAT I'D RATHER DRIVE ANYWAY."
WHAT'S THAT PINGING SOUND, FRED? IS THE MYSTERY MACHINE SUPPOSED TO BE RATTLING LIKE THAT?
IT SURE IS, VELMA.
IT SURE IS.
THE MYSTERY MACHINE
PING PING PING PING
The End

BURNS CASTLE, SCOTLAND.

WE HEARD *RAPPING* ON OUR *WALLS!*
THERE'S A *COLD* SPOT IN OUR *ROOM!*

SOMEONE KEEPS PUTTING THE TOILET SEAT UP IN OUR BATHROOM.
-HEH-HEH-
ISN'T THIS PLACE GREAT?

WHAT ABOUT YOU? HAVE *YOU* EXPERIENCED THE GHOST YET?
NO. NOT YET.

WE'RE HEADING TO THE THIRD FLOOR. THEY SAY YOU CAN HEAR HER WEEPING IN A BROOM CLOSET THERE. COMING?
NO, THANK YOU.
I THINK WE'RE GOING TO CALL IT A NIGHT.
CHEER UP, GREG. WE STILL HAVE TWO NIGHTS HERE.
THAT GIVES US PLENTY OF CHANCES TO SEE...

...THE GHOST!
AND SHE'S EMPTYING MY WALLET!
THE GHOSTLY GUEST
JOHN ROZUM-WRITER
KAREN MATCHETTE-PENCILLER
STEPHEN DESTEFANO-INKER • PAUL BECTON-COLORS
NICK J NAPOLITANO-LETTERER • SNO CONE-SEPARATIONS
HARVEY RICHARDS-ASST EDITOR • JOAN HILTY-EDITOR

GEE, MRS. BURNS, IT WAS AWFULLY KIND OF YOU TO FLY US OUT HERE...

...BUT I'M GUESSING THERE WAS A REASON OTHER THAN YOU FEELING GENEROUS.
I ONLY WISH GENEROSITY HAD SOMETHING TO DO WITH IT.
TO BE FRANK, IT TOOK SOME DOING TO SCRAPE TOGETHER THE MONEY FOR YOUR AIR FARE.

BUT, I WAS DESPERATE AND DIDN'T SEE ANY ALTERNATIVE.
WHAT DO YOU MEAN?

THIS CASTLE HAS BELONGED TO MY FAMILY FOR GENERATIONS. I'D LIKE TO SEE THAT IT STAYS IN THE FAMILY. MY BROTHER, REGINALD, DOESN'T SHARE MY VIEWS.
THE COST OF UPKEEP ON A PROPERTY THIS LARGE IS ASTRONOMICAL. MY FAMILY NO LONGER HAS THE MONEY TO MAINTAIN IT.

SO WE STARTED RENTING OUT THE OTHER HALF OF THE CASTLE AS A VACATION RETREAT.
--RATHER THAN SELL IT, LIKE I WISHED!

WELL, WE NEVER HAD TROUBLE BOOKING ANY OF THE GUEST SUITES-- UNTIL LATELY.
I'M SORRY TO HEAR THAT, BUT I STILL DON'T UNDERSTAND WHAT IT HAS TO DO WITH US.

WHILE THEY'RE TALKING, LET'S SEE WHAT IT SAYS ABOUT THE FOOD.
HOPEFULLY MRS. BURNS HASN'T HAD TO CUT CORNERS THERE.
THIS IS SO AWKWARD. YOU SEE WE'RE HAVING A LITTLE TROUBLE WITH A...GHOST...
WELCOME TO BURNS CASTLE
CASTLE CUISINE

DID YOU SAY "GUEST"?
...PIES, GAME HENS, MUTTON...
...RHOST...

WHERE DOES IT SAY "TOAST"?
I SAID "GHOST."

ZOINKS! LIKE, NO THANKS, I'LL STICK WITH THE MUTTON!
REE TOO!
CASTLE CUISINE

HERE IT IS IN THE "HAUNTED INNS OF SCOTLAND" GUIDEBOOK.
"FOR AS LONG AS ANYONE CAN REMEMBER, THE HALLS OF BURNS CASTLE HAVE BEEN ROAMED BY THE GHOST OF A GIRL IN HER TWENTIES...
"...AFFECTIONATELY REFERRED TO AS 'WEEPING WINNIE.'
"WHILE SELDOM SEEN, SHE MAKES HERSELF KNOWN BY RAPPING ON WALLS, REORGANIZING ROOM ITEMS, AND THE SOUNDS OF HER CRYING."

LIKE, IF I EXPERIENCE ANY OF THOSE THINGS, I'LL BE CRYING TOO!
BOO HOO HOO HOO
REE TOO!
LIKE, I MEANT CRYING OUT LIKE THIS...
HELP! GHOST! GET ME OUT OF HERE!

SHAGGY, WILL YOU KNOCK IT OFF?
IF MRS. BURNS IS RIGHT, THEN "WEEPING WINNIE" HAS STARTED A NEW HABIT--
--STEALING.
SMASH!
WHEN I TOLD YOU TWO TO KNOCK IT OFF, I MEANT YOUR FOOLING AROUND.
NOW, LOOK WHAT YOU'VE DONE!
RUS?
YOU'RE KIDDING, RIGHT? LIKE, WE ARE NOWHERE NEAR THAT TABLE OVER THERE. WHY DON'T YOU POINT YOUR FINGER AT SOMEONE ELSE, LIKE THE...

...RHOST!
...GHOST!

THAT'S ENOUGH FOR ME. I VOTE WE GO HOME.
REE TOO.
I CAN'T BELIEVE PEOPLE ARE ACTUALLY WILLING TO PAY MONEY TO STAY HERE, SO THEY CAN SEE A GHOST.

THAT'S JUST IT, SHAGGY. NOW THAT THE GHOST IS STEALING FROM THE GUESTS, PEOPLE WON'T COME NEAR BURNS CASTLE.
I HAVE A HUNCH THAT THE SOLUTION TO THIS MYSTERY CAN BE FOUND ON THE THIRD FLOOR OF THE BURNS FAMILY SIDE OF THE CASTLE.
THAT'S WHERE REGINALD LIVES.

NEVER MIND WHAT CAN BE FOUND IN THE OTHER HALF OF THE CASTLE. DOES ANYONE REMEMBER HOW TO FIND OUR ROOMS?
THEY'RE RIGHT BEHIND ME, MISS. THE LAST TWO DOORS ON THE LEFT. I JUST FINISHED MAKING THEM UP FOR YOU.
OF COURSE, I FEEL SO SILLY. THANK YOU.
NOT AT ALL. THIS CASTLE IS A MAZE OF DOORS AND PASSAGEWAYS. IT'S EASY TO LOSE YOUR WAY HERE.

I SAY WE ALL GET A LITTLE REST. THEN WE'LL GET BACK TOGETHER AND TRY TO COME UP WITH A PLAN.

ZOINKS! IT LOOKS LIKE OUR PILFERING POLTERGEIST HAS STRUCK AGAIN!

LIKE, THIS BOX OF SCOOBY SNACKS WAS FULL BEFORE WE WENT TO MEET MRS. BURNS. NOW, LOOK AT IT.
WHY WOULD A GHOST WANT TO STEAL SCOOBY SNACKS?
Scooby Snacks

LIKE, WHO ELSE COULD IT HAVE BEEN? I WAS THE LAST ONE OUT OF THE ROOM, EXCEPT FOR SCOOB, BUT HE SAID HE'D LOCK UP BEHIND HIM.
I THINK YOU'RE BARKING UP THE WRONG TREE, SHAGGY. I'M CERTAIN THE GHOST ISN'T TO BLAME HERE.
NO, BUT IT GIVES ME AN IDEA.
LISTEN UP, GANG.
Scooby Snacks
TWENTY MINUTES LATER.
WE'RE SUPPOSED TO MEET THE OTHERS IN THE DINING ROOM.
I HROPE REE CAN FRIND IT.
I JUST HOPE THEY LEFT US SOME FOOD.

BOO!
CAUGHT IN THE ACT!
AFTER HER!

LOOK, SHE'S WALKING RIGHT THROUGH THE WALL!
I DON'T THINK SO!

WHOOF!
HOW DID YOU KNOW?
IF SHE COULD WALK THROUGH THE WALL, THEN WHY DID SHE NEED A KEY TO OPEN THE DOOR TO YOUR ROOM?

FREDDIE, ARE YOU SURE SHE DIDN'T GO DOWNSTAIRS?
THE SERVANTS' QUARTERS ARE UPSTAIRS.

SHE'S GETTING AWAY!

HELP ME! I CONFESS. PLEASE, I'LL TELL YOU EVERYTHING.
SLAM
SLAM
BANG!
BANG
BANG! BANG! BANG!

IT'S THE MAID, NOT REGINALD AT ALL.
I WAS AFRAID REGINALD WOULD SELL THE CASTLE, AND I'D BE OUT OF WORK.
SHE USED HER KNOWLEDGE OF ALL THE HIDDEN DOORS AND PASSAGEWAYS TO MAKE IT SEEM LIKE HER EXITS AND ENTRANCES WERE SUPERNATURAL.

AND HER PASS KEY TO GET IN AND OUT OF THE ROOMS.
SHE ALREADY KNEW WHERE THE VALUABLES WERE, FROM CLEANING THE ROOMS.

THAT SOLVES THE THEFTS, BUT SHAGGY AND SCOOBY, HOW DID YOU MANAGE TO CLOSE ALL THOSE DOORS AT ONCE? IT'S ALMOST LIKE YOU HAD A LITTLE HELP!
LIKE, DON'T LOOK AT US, WE JUST GOT HERE...
...AND WE STILL HAVEN'T FOUND THE DINING ROOM!
END

MUSEUM MAYHEM
DARRYL TAYLOR KRAVITZ DOTH WRITE
ROBERT POPE YE PENCILER
SCOTT MCRAE EARL OF INK
HEROIC AGE DUKE OF COLORS
O LETTERS- MIKE SELLERS
ROYAL COUNT OF EDITOR JEANINE SCHAEFER
AHHHHH!
MY HISTORY REPORT ISN'T WORTH THIS!
AHHHHH!

THE NEXT NIGHT MYSTERY, INC. IS CALLED AND IS ON THE CASE.
THANK YOU FOR ARRIVING ON SUCH SHORT NOTICE. THESE GHOSTS HAVE BROUGHT MUSEUM ATTENDANCE TO A STAND STILL.
NO, PROBLEM, MR. DANIELS!

GRACEN, THE LAST CURATOR, LEFT BECAUSE OF THESE GHOSTS. HE WAS WORKING LATE AND WAS SO SCARED HE QUIT.

CRASH!

A FEW MORE LOUD CRASHES AND MOMENTS LATER.
LIKE, SCOOB, HOW DID I KNOW THAT, LIKE, TOUCHING ONE ARM ON A SUIT OF ARMOR WOULD CAUSE FIVE OF THEM TO FALL?

MEANWHILE IN THE ARMOR ROOM, EVIDENCE ABOUNDS BUT WHAT COULD THE CLUES MEAN?
THERE IS GREASE AROUND THE BOTTOM OF THIS CASE.
IT WOULD HAVE TAKEN MORE THAN ONE PERSON TO LIFT THIS COVER.
SOMEONE NEEDED A LOT OF TIME TO COMMIT THESE CRIMES.

WHAT ARE THOSE KIDS DOING HERE? THEY'LL RUIN EVERYTHING!

BACK TO ... YOU KNOW ...THE EGYPTIAN ROOM
SCOOB, LIKE, THERE MUST BE A ZILLION DOLLARS OF GOLD AND STATUES IN THIS PLACE. LIKE WE HAVE TO BE REAL CAREFUL!

RIKES! RA ROMIC ROOK ROFFIN!

LIKE, THAT'S NOT A COMIC BOOK COFFIN! IT WAS, LIKE, WHERE THESE PEOPLE BURIED THEIR KINGS AND QUEENS.

RAAAA
RAAAA

RACHOO!

WHAM
LIKE, WE DID IT NOW! LIKE, I'M GOING TO HAVE TO GET A MILLION HOUSE PAPER ROUTE TO PAY FOR THIS!

LIKE, THIS BOX IS THE HIDDEN LIGHT SWITCH FOR THE ROOM!

LET'S FLIP THEM ON!

MEANWHILE...

THEY FOUND MY HOLOGRAM SWITCHES. I HAVE TO GET AWAY!

AHHH!

LATER, MR. DANIELS IS ALERTED AND THE CRIME IS EXPOSED.
GRACEN HAD SET UP HOLOGRAM GHOSTS TO SCARE PEOPLE AWAY. HE CONTROLLED THEM FROM A SWITCH BOX IN THE EGYPTIAN ROOM.

THE GREASE NEAR THE CASE WAS FROM A FORKLIFT HE USED OFF HOURS TO REMOVE THE ITEMS SO NO ONE WOULD PAY ATTENTION TO THE EGYPTIAN ROOM.
WE CHECKED AND THE MISSING ARTIFACTS ARE MISLABELED IN THE WAREHOUSE.

THAT TREASURE WAS MINE! I FOUND IT! I NEEDED TIME TO GET THE TREASURE MAP OUT OF THE EGYPTIAN COFFIN. I DIDN'T COUNT ON YOU KIDS INTERFERING.

AND, LIKE, OUR SECRET WEAPON... SCOOBY-DOO!
THE END